YORK NOTES

Translations

Brian Friel

Note by John Brannigan

D1015915

Longman   York Press

YORK PRESS
322 Old Brompton Road, London SW5 9JH

PEARSON EDUCATION LIMITED
Edinburgh Gate, Harlow,
Essex CM20 2JE, United Kingdom
Associated companies, branches and representatives throughout the world

First published 2000
Fourth impression 2002

ISBN 0-582-41475-X

Designed by Vicki Pacey
Phototypeset by Gem Graphics, Trenance, Mawgan Porth, Cornwall
Colour reproduction and film output by Spectrum Colour
Produced by Pearson Education North Asia Limited, Hong Kong

Contents

(Italicised numbers in the glossaries refer to the page numbers of the original text)

INTRODUCTION

HOW TO STUDY A PLAY

Studying on your own requires self-discipline and a carefully thought-out work plan in order to be effective.

- Drama is a special kind of writing (the technical term is 'genre') because it needs a performance in the theatre to arrive at a full interpretation of its meaning. Try to imagine that you are a member of the audience when reading the play. Think about how it could be presented on the stage, not just about the words on the page.

- Drama is always about conflict of some sort (which may be below the surface). Identify the conflicts in the play and you will be close to identifying the large ideas or themes which bind all the parts together.

- Make careful notes on themes, character, plot and any sub-plots of the play.

- Why do you like or dislike the characters in the play? How do your feelings towards them develop and change?

- Playwrights find non-realistic ways of allowing an audience to see into the minds and motives of their characters, for example soliloquy, aside or music. Consider how such dramatic devices are used in the play you are studying.

- Think of the playwright writing the play. Why were these particular arrangements of events, characters and speeches chosen?

- Cite exact sources for all quotations, whether from the text itself or from critical commentaries. Wherever possible find your own examples from the play to back up your opinions.

- Always express your ideas in your own words.

This York Note offers an introduction to *Translations* and cannot substitute for close reading of the text and the study of secondary sources.

Since its first performance in 1980, *Translations* has entertained, informed and disturbed audiences around the world. It has been performed regularly in Ireland, England and the United States, and has been widely acclaimed by critics as a classic of modern drama. It is indeed a play with an unusual power to show the best and the worst of human relationships and feelings, to combine comedy and tragedy to their fullest potential. *Translations* examines the impact of linguistic, cultural and political change on the lives and feelings of a handful of individuals in a small Irish village in 1833, and in doing so it shows us the human capacity for love, hatred, jealousy, humour, survival and destruction. It allows us first to enjoy the humour and drama of everyday relationships at a leisurely pace, but then moves through a rapid succession of traumatic changes to arrive at its tense, tragic conclusion.

Friel's play is concerned with the effect of historical changes on individuals and communities, and the play raises important questions about the nature of history, community, language and identity. Hugh, the school master, tells us that 'It is not the literal past, the "facts" of history, that shape us, but images of the past embodied in language ... we must never cease renewing those images' (p. 66). *Translations* could be seen as a play that does exactly what Hugh describes. It takes images from Irish history – of peasants with a love of learning, of English soldiers trampling the crops under their feet, of the people trying to eke out a living for themselves – and it renews those images. In doing so, it tells a story of love, war, misunderstanding, loyalty and betrayal. It can be read as a complex lesson specifically on Irish history, or it can be read as a tale of any two communities which are bitterly divided. It is not a simple play, and can be interpreted in many different ways, but this is what makes it a rich and rewarding work of drama.

Translations was first produced on stage in 1980 in Derry city in Northern Ireland. It was an instant success, and its first run was sold out. It received many excellent reviews and has remained a popular play ever since. This seems to be at odds with its rather obscure subject matter. The play is set in a hedge-school in a Gaelic-speaking area of northwestern Ireland in 1833 – not the most obvious recipe for theatrical success. The events depicted in the play – involving an ordnance survey project and the introduction of a national system of elementary education – were unknown except to small academic circles. Reviewers seemed to be particularly impressed by two devices in the play, however. The first was the means by which Friel's play had the audience believe that they were hearing both Gaelic and English languages spoken when the play was presented entirely in English. The second was the powerful scene in Act II in which Yolland and Maire, an English soldier and an Irish peasant girl, find a way of conveying their love for each other without having a common language.

The dramatic devices of the play were innovative and original certainly, but the play had, and still has, a popular appeal which went beyond the admiration of theatre critics. *Translations* seemed to summarise, through events of local significance, the story of how one nation lost its language, culture and literature as a result of being conquered by another nation. It articulated the tragedy of Irish history over the course of several hundred years by telling a story about several days in the life of a fictitious Irish village in 1833. For those who were not versed in Irish history, the play offered a parable about the fate of an insular, antiquated people when they were exposed to an adventurous and modern empire. Because the people were insular and antiquated, they could not be translated into the modern world, and so were lost in the mists of time. This is why the play ends with Hugh struggling to remember what had happened to another lost civilisation, the Carthaginians.

While the play was immensely popular, it was also deeply controversial, not least because it was found to contain some serious distortions of historical facts. Reviewers and commentators pointed to exaggerations of the violence attributed to the soldiers who undertook the ordnance survey, errors in the depiction of the survey as a military campaign, and misrepresentations of the process of changing place-names. It was criticised as a biased, inaccurate account of the events it purported to represent, and one historian despaired that it would be accepted by audiences as the truth when there were so many errors in it. Friel was aware of having shaped and altered the historical facts for the purposes of dramatic fiction, however. The soldiers of the ordnance survey did not carry bayonets and did not order evictions, but the point is that other English soldiers did. The accuracy of events in the play is not so important as what those events represent. Friel wanted to show that the renaming of Irish villages and townlands had as destructive an effect on Irish culture and society as a military invasion on Irish people.

The play was first produced at a time when the conflict in Northern Ireland between the British army and paramilitary organisations was particularly intense. Some critics believed that the play was simply exploiting the past to offer an anti-British interpretation of the present conflict. But the play is more complex in its representation of history and politics than this. The characters and incidents in the play do bear some relation to the war in Northern Ireland in the 1970s, but *Translations* has a great deal to say about language, translation, cultural differences and similarities, about the consequences of local, seemingly minor events in history and about the impact of historical and national changes on individuals, and these aspects of the play do not correspond exactly with such a reading.

Friel seems to be interested, not in giving us a one-sided story of events, but in the dilemmas and choices which have the potential to affect the course of history. In many of Friel's plays, at a precise moment in time, individuals face a dilemma which must be resolved, and which will have a decisive effect. In *Translations*, to take one example, Owen and Yolland face the dilemma of what to call a place called 'Tobair Vree', which is named after a man who fell down a well there. Owen asks: 'Do we scrap Tobair Vree altogether and call it – what? – The Cross? Crossroads? Or do we keep piety with a man long dead, long forgotten, his name "eroded" beyond recognition, whose trivial little story nobody in the parish remembers?' (p. 44). Friel indicates that the answer to the question will affect the future of Irish language, culture and history, even if only in a small, local way.

The achievement of Brian Friel in *Translations* is that he brings us to the realisation that every little, personal, local story – of love, hope, loss and change – is connected intimately and subtly to the course of history. As to what each story means, and how each character should have dealt with her or his dilemma, he leaves that open to you.

PART TWO

SUMMARIES & COMMENTARIES

Brian Friel's Translations *was published first by Faber & Faber in 1981, following the first performance of the play in the Guildhall in Derry on 23 September 1980 by the Field Day Theatre Company. This remains the standard edition, and is the edition used in this Note.* Translations *is also available in an anthology of Irish drama and criticism, which includes notes and critical writings on the play. This edition can be found in John P. Harrington, ed.,* Modern Irish Drama, *Norton & Company, 1991.*

SYNOPSIS

The play opens with Manus, the school master's son, trying to teach Sarah how to speak. The local people believe that Sarah is dumb, but Manus helps her to speak her name. They begin with basic breathing exercises – 'relax and breathe in' – and mouth movements – 'Get your tongue and your lips moving' – and then Manus encourages Sarah to speak – 'My name is -'. This simple lesson at the beginning of the play introduces the main theme of the play, the problems of communication, language and translation which have been the root causes of violence and conflict. Communication is difficult, and is always an act of translation – from thought to words, from one language to another, from one culture to another. When Sarah succeeds in speaking her name, she is making the first act of translation in the play, translating silence into speech. In the final Act of the play, however, Sarah returns to silence, and this is just one example of the failures of communication which resound through the play.

    Translations is about the relationships between people who speak different languages and come from different cultures. It presents a stark opposition between the Irish people of Baile Beag who speak Gaelic and who trace their roots to ancient civilisation and the English soldiers who speak English and who seem to be unaware of much outside their own culture. Manus, Doalty and Bridget are suspicious of the soldiers, and suspect that the map the soldiers are making is not so harmless as Owen wants them to believe. On the other hand, Hugh and Maire seem to tolerate, and even like, the presence of the soldiers. There are differences in how the English soldiers react to the Irish characters too. Lancey treats the people of Baile Beag with indifference at first, and brutally towards the end of the play. Yolland, however, falls in love with the people and the place, describing it as 'really heavenly'. But even for the characters who are enthusiastic to communicate with each other, as is the case with Yolland and Maire, there are problems with language and translation between the two cultures which have tragic consequences in store.

It is the tension between these characters from different cultures and with very different personalities which propels the action of the play forward. Friel's play examines the impact of political conflicts on human relationships in one small community in a few days. For Yolland, Maire, Owen, Manus, Lancey and Hugh, the events of those few days test their allegiances and aspirations. Act I establishes the identities of the characters, and situates them in relation to each other. In Act II, some of the characters are shown responding to changes in their circumstances. Owen and Yolland must gauge their own feelings about the changes which they are participating in imposing on Baile Beag and the surrounding areas. Maire and Yolland struggle to find a way of communicating their feelings to each other despite language and cultural barriers. In the final Act, circumstances change beyond the control of the characters. Lancey is forced to respond to the disappearance of Yolland. The inhabitants of Baile Beag must examine their own feelings about the brutal response of the English soldiers.

Although there are comic and entertaining scenes in the play, in the concluding Act it becomes more sombre and tragic. It is presumed that the Donnelly twins have harmed Yolland in some way 'as a gesture'. But gestures usually invite replies, and Lancey replies with the language of violence and threat. The undercurrents of distrust and misunderstanding which pervade between the characters in the rest of the play come out in the open in the final Act, in which we see the lasting damage of divided political and cultural loyalties. The people of Baile Beag feel that they are dispossessed of their ancient traditions and ways of life, and that they are poised on the brink of disaster. Hugh's loss of memory, and his talk of a community which could have been idyllic but which was instead destroyed, illustrate this **tragedy** as the play draws to a close.

DETAILED SUMMARIES & COMMENTARIES

ACT I   In a hedge-school in the townland of Baile Beag

Manus is teaching Sarah how to speak, while an old man, 'the infant prodigy' – Jimmy Jack – shares his enjoyment of classical literature. They are waiting for Hugh O'Donnell, the school master, to turn up, but he is late, attending a christening celebration. Other pupils turn up for class, including Maire, to whom Manus seems to pay a lot of attention. Bridget and Doalty are excited when they appear, because Doalty has stolen a piece of equipment from the soldiers who are surveying the land nearby. When Hugh turns up, he is slightly drunk, and he begins to tell the class news of the soldiers and their work in making an ordnance survey of the area. He explains that he has invited the officer in charge of the ordnance survey to talk to the pupils about the purposes of the survey.

Hugh is interrupted by Maire, who complains that she wants to learn English, a language which will be much more useful if she is to emigrate to England or America than the Greek and Latin which Hugh is teaching them. Hugh ignores her, and proceeds to tell them about the opening of the new national school nearby, in which, he says, he is to be the new headmaster. Hugh is then interrupted by the arrival of his son, Owen, 'dressed smartly – a city man'. He is a merchant in Dublin and has been hired as a translator with the English soldiers who are engaged in the ordnance survey. Owen introduces two English officers, Captain Lancey and Lieutenant Yolland, to the others, and translates Lancey's announcements about the purpose of the survey. But Owen does not translate exactly what Lancey is saying, and Manus reprimands him afterwards for neglecting to translate Lancey's statement that the survey would serve military as well as civil purposes. Yolland, meanwhile, is shy and reserved, and says very little.

The first act of *Translations* defines clearly the characters and relationships which will be the focus of the rest of the play. In drama, characters are usually first experienced by sight, that is, when they first appear on stage. There are notable exceptions in this play. Hugh and the English soldiers are mentioned before they are seen. This alerts the audience to the importance of these characters, who are obviously of great interest to the others. But for those characters who are not mentioned, their first appearance on stage establishes in the audience's minds something of their personality, and how they fit into the story. The physical appearance and 'shabby' dress of Manus (p. 11), for example, distinguishes him from his brother, Owen, who is dressed 'smartly' (p. 26). Hugh enters 'shabbily dressed, carrying a stick' (p. 23). Each of these visual details tells us a lot about the characteristics of each person. Manus's shabby appearance tells us that he is poor and down-to-earth. Owen, on the other hand, has pulled himself out of poverty to a more comfortable lifestyle, and is more pretentious than Manus. Hugh is dressed shabbily like Manus, but his stick conveys his air of dignity and, of course, his pomposity.

It is in details such as these that the differences and tensions between the characters are revealed. Lancey's appearance, for example, is described as 'crisp'. This contrasts with Hugh's slight drunkenness and slovenliness. These are, on one level, differences merely in personality. But they are also emblematic of wider cultural and social differences between them, which account partly for the conflict between the Irish and English characters. Lancey is proud of his 'crisp' manner, and, in his eyes, it marks him out as superior to the 'foreign civilians'. Hugh values words and learning, which is evident in his enthusiasm for knowledge and literature, and does not value appearances or material wealth, which is obvious from his own style of dress. Hugh and Lancey hold two very different sets of values and beliefs, then, and the differences between them are reflected in the actions and events of the rest of the play.

11 **hedge-school** under the penal laws in the seventeenth century, a Catholic or Gaelic-language education was outlawed in Ireland. In defiance, Irish people set up mobile, secret schools which were initially in hedgerows with a look-out nearby to warn of English officials or soldiers. When the laws were relaxed the schools moved to barns or cow-sheds, like the one in the

play. The schools taught arithmetic, writing, Latin, Greek, and Gaelic history and literature. Parents paid small sums, or paid in kind, to the masters for the education of their children, or themselves. By the 1820s there were roughly half a million children being educated through the hedge-schools, which became obsolete with the introduction of compulsory free 'national schools', which taught in English and were part of the state system (see Historical Background)

byre cow-shed

battle of hay a small bale of hay

the Infant Prodigy an ironic name for Jimmy Jack, who is in his sixties, and is always the first to answer the school master correctly. It indicates that he has always been at the same precocious level of ability, and yet he is unlikely to advance further

Homer reputedly the author of two famous Greek epics, *The Iliad* and *The Odyssey*, thought to have lived sometime between the ninth and seventh centuries BC. His writings formed the basis of elementary education in ancient Greece, and contain the classic tales of Greek mythology. He became important in English culture in the eighteenth century. Though classics would have been taught in many of the Irish hedge-schools Jimmy Jack reading Homer in Greek indicates that he is at an advanced stage of learning

Baile Beag (Gaelic) small town. It may suggest that the community represented in the play could be anywhere. Friel is also contrasting the 'small', limited scope of such a community, its insularity, with the greater opportunities and capacities of the big town, Baile Mor

13 **Athene** goddess of wisdom of the city and of civilisation, and daughter of Zeus. Jimmy Jack is reading the passage from Book XIII of *The Odyssey* in which Athene of the flashing eyes appears to Ulysses to tell him that she will guide him through his ordeals and lead him in his return home

Ulysses also known as Odysseus. *The Odyssey* is the story of his wanderings after the Trojan war, and of his many adventures on his return home to resume the throne of Ithaca. Renowned as a cunning and courageous schemer, able to overcome all kinds of battles and trials by his stealth and persistence

Diarmuid's Grania (from Irish mythology, in the Fenian tales) Grania was daughter of the High King, Cormac Mac Airt. She was to marry the renowned old warrior, Fionn Mac Cumhaill. To avoid marrying him, she used

druidic magic to send everyone at the feast before the wedding asleep,
except for Diarmuid. She demanded that he rescue her from the marriage,
and put a spell on him. Fionn was angry on discovering that the two had
fled, and so began his pursuit of them. Although Diarmuid resisted Grania's
demands, he soon fell in love with her, and the gods and kings persuaded
Fionn to forget his anger. Grania represents passion, ruthlessness and
independence. For the Irish characters of *Translations*, Greek and Irish
mythological heroes rub shoulders – an unusual perspective in Western
Europe, where Greek and Roman myths are much more widely known than
Irish ones

Artemis goddess of the young, and daughter of Zeus, renowned as a
huntress, armed with bow and quiver, and patroness of young women
athletes

Helen of Troy renowned as the most beautiful woman in the world, and
daughter of Zeus. To avert war, her many suitors made a pact that whoever
married her would be protected by the others. She married Menelaus, king
of Sparta, but was abducted by Paris who carried her off to Troy. The Greek
leaders, including Ulysses, organised the campaign to win her back, and so
began the Trojan War. Her fame rests then on being so beautiful that she
sparked off a war

Zeus the most powerful god in Greek mythology, ruler of the heavens. He is
known for his power, ruling over the fate of humankind, and wielding
weapons of thunder and lightning. But he is also known for his love affairs,
and for the many offspring these produced

15 **Would I be safe?** Maire is referring to Jimmy's obsession with the goddesses
of his reading, and asking jokingly if he will show a similar sexual obsession
with her. His reply suggests that his interest in women does not go beyond
his reading

Esne fatigata? Jimmy has switched to speaking Latin

Fit me better if I had even that much English the first sign to the audience
that the characters are supposed to be speaking in the Irish language

'In Norfolk we besport …' this line is spoken as if awkward to Maire's
tongue, and its archaic diction suggests that it has been passed down from
an old book, or through many generations, as a source of amusement.
Painted in colourful spiral stripes, maypoles were erected in England's
village greens or town squares, and people would dance around them on
May Day. Although Irish people had some festivals to mark the beginning of

summer, including the 'Queen of the May', the custom of maypole dancing
was not observed. Maire mispronounces the word as 'maypoll', indicating
that she does not understand it, in much the same way as Yolland will later
mispronounce Irish words. It is supposed to be the first example of English
spoken in the play, and significantly it is one of a number of references to
celebrations of beginnings – summer begins, Hugh attends a baptism,
Yolland speaks of 1789 in France as Year One, and Sarah begins to speak
her name

16 **Sure you know I have only Irish like yourself** at this point the play confirms to
the audience that the characters are supposed to be speaking in the Irish
language

Bo-som Jimmy pronounces this word awkwardly, indicating that it is not in
his native language. It suggests, like his earlier ruminations on Homer's
goddesses, that he is obsessed with sexual matters

Diana Roman name for Greek goddess, Artemis

Nova Scotia province on east coast of Canada, one of the closest parts of
North America to Ireland

new national schools the hedge-schools had become so widespread in the
early nineteenth century that they had almost become a national institution.
In response to the growing demand for education, Chief Secretary Stanley
devised in 1831 a state system of education which became known as the
national schools. Whereas the hedge-schools were outlawed and were
organised informally within local communities, the national schools were
state-run and were provided free of charge at elementary or primary level.
The English language was the sole medium of instruction in the new
national schools, and they were therefore partly responsible for the decline
in importance of the Irish language (see Historical Background)

17 **sapper** a soldier of the Royal Engineers

surveyor's pole a striped pole which land surveyors use to take
measurements and angles

Red Coats (colloquial) soldiers of the British army who traditionally wore red
uniforms

18 **Just to indicate ... a presence** Manus is suggesting that we can interpret
Doalty's stealing the surveyor's pole as a rebellious act, not just a prank

a great aul shaft for your churn Doalty is suggesting on one level that the
surveyor's pole could be useful to Bridget to stir the butter in her churn, but
he is also making a crude sexual innuendo here, hence Bridget's reaction

18 **bucks** (slang) men, as male deer, rabbit or hare

19 **Satires of Horace** Horace (65–8BC) was a Roman lyric poet and satirist, famous for his *Odes* and *Epistles*. Dan Doalty is making fun of Jimmy Jack's absorption in the classics in suggesting that 'Nellie Ruadh's aul fella' wants Jimmy to recite Horace's satires for him

Virgil's *Georgics* Virgil (70–19BC) celebrated Roman poet, renowned for his poem on the founding of Rome, *The Aeneid*, and for his *Eclogues* and *Georgics*. Jimmy Jack quotes from Virgil to instruct Doalty that he should be planting corn in his field with black soil. This suggests again Jimmy Jack's absorption in the classics, that he relies upon the ancient poems and tales for practical agricultural tips as well as beautiful verse and stories

at the salmon fishing for salmon

the Donnelly twins ... Haven't seen them their absence suggests that they are engaged in mischief, particularly from the manner in which Doalty seems to be evasive about them, and whistles after telling Manus that he hasn't seen them, hinting that he knows more than he has revealed. Bridget then informs Manus that two of the soldiers' horses were found at the bottom of a cliff, casting suspicion on the Donnelly twins

20 **'It's easier to stamp out learning than to recall it'** quoted from Tacitus's *Life of Agricola*, the Roman commander who ruled over Britain in the first century AD and who conquered parts of northern England and southern Scotland. The quotation has particular relevance to the play's theme, in that *Translations* is depicting a culture of learning and scholarship that has been stamped out by the English colonisation of Ireland

passage money in the nineteenth century, because of Ireland's poor economic conditions, over 8 million emigrated, mostly to the USA, from where by convention, family members would send back money to pay for others to emigrate. This money was known as passage money

no man in the house Maire is implying here the limited options available for women in nineteenth-century Ireland, particularly in large families in which the father has died and there are no adult brothers. With no man in her house to bring in a steady income, she faces the prospect either of marrying someone with a stable job who can provide for her family, or emigrating to find work herself so that she can send money back to support her family

21 **the sweet smell** the smell of rotting potatoes. In the early nineteenth century, because of a huge population increase, Irish people came to depend on the potato crop which was easily grown and which provided a lot of nutrition. But crops failed several times during the early nineteenth century, including the year in which the play is set. Between 1845 and 1850 crops failed completely, causing the death of over 1 million people, and forcing over 1 million more to emigrate. This catastrophe, known as the Great Famine, had a devastating impact on the Irish people, and on the Irish language, as many of the remaining Irish speakers in Ireland were hit hardest by the Famine. This smell of potato blight, which also occurs at the end of the play, signals the disaster which is only twelve years away for small rural communities like the one depicted in the play (see Historical Background)

St. Colmcille one of the great Christian monks of ancient Ireland, who lived through the sixth century, and founded influential monasteries in Doire (now Derry or Londonderry), and on Iona. Being born in Donegal where the play is set, the saint is particularly famous there, but Doalty is inventing the prophecy that there would never be potato blight in Baile Beag

22 **Buncrana people** Buncrana is a town close to where the play is set. Bridget is suggesting a difference between the people of the small community of Baile Beag and the more urban, modern ('cute') people of the larger town. 'Cute' might suggest that they are more cultivated and modern, but perhaps also crafty and devious

yella meal yellow meal, finely ground and used for porridge. An equivalent term would be 'mincemeat'

jouk (colloquial) look

23 **I'm dying about you** I really like you

Eamon Donal from Tor Bridget now knows who the father of the child is, as Nellie Ruadh promised to name the child after its father, who had previously been unknown to the others

24 **Pliny Minor** Gaius Plinius Caecilius Secundus (AD62–c.112), nephew of Pliny the Elder, and a Roman letter-writer. An administrator in the Roman empire, he is most renowned for his description of the eruption of Vesuvius

Sophocles from Colonus Greek playwright (496–406BC), famous for his Theban plays and the character of Oedipus. Hugh is mocking Dan Doalty's abilities as a student by comparing him with Sophocles, but quoting Sophocles telling us that ignorance is bliss

25 **commerce ... particularly suited** Hugh is scornful of the English language, which reflects no tradition of learning and honour, and is used only for

conducting business. To Hugh, who has an aristocrat's aloof attitude to commerce, the English language is base because it is tainted by its materialistic uses. But notice the irony of what Hugh says next. He calls for bread, thereby showing that his own language is also used for daily business. And his criticism of English for being too commercial comes not long after he has just collected fees from his students. He also shows himself later to be unaware of one the most famous of English poets, William Wordsworth

our own culture ... happier conjugation Again, Hugh is mocking the English language by suggesting that Gaelic and the classical languages are better suited to each other, and that English is less easy to trace to classical roots. There is irony here too, for, with the play conducted in English, and Hugh constantly asking his students to explain the derivations of Latin words, the play is showing us that English has a close relationship with the classical languages too

English ... couldn't really express us more irony, given the language in which the play is conducted

Dan O'Connell Daniel O'Connell (1775–1847), political leader, barrister and Catholic landowner, who rose to prominence as a campaigner for Catholic emancipation and became known as the Liberator. O'Connell organised a nationwide mass movement to remove the prohibition on Catholics sitting as MPs, which was achieved in 1829. By organising the campaign through mass rallies across Ireland, he contributed much to the widespread politicisation of the Irish people, where previously local politics tended to overshadow national issues. He was controversial, however, on the language question, suggesting, as Maire says, that Gaelic was 'a barrier to modern progress'. When Hugh refers to him as 'that little Kerry politician', he is being sarcastic, as O'Connell's reputation was well established throughout Ireland by the time in which the play is set, 1833. The principal street in Dublin was renamed O'Connell Street at the beginning of the twentieth century (see Historical Background)

I want English Maire demands to be taught English, knowing that if she is to have a chance of success in England or America, or even in the more urbanised parts of Ireland, she will need to know it, rather than Latin or Greek

26 **Mr George Alexander** the name suggests an Englishman, or a man of English descent. This was typical for men in positions of power in Ireland

in colonial times, particularly in positions of trust, such as 'Justice of the Peace'

26 **Euripides** Greek dramatist (480–406BC), and contemporary of Sophocles; renowned for his tragedies

a city man Owen is dressed to appear different to the other natives of Baile Beag, as he has become a businessman in Dublin. His modern, smart dress will distinguish him from the peasant appearance of his father's pupils. The others joke with him about his wealth, and it is uncertain from his replies whether or not he is wealthy. He is on the payroll of the army as a translator, however, which would suggest that he isn't a rich man

Hugh Mor O'Donnell Owen is addressing his father as Hugh O'Donnell the great. 'Mor' means big, and signifies seniority and prestige in Gaelic families

27 **poteen** home-brewed alcoholic drink, made from potatoes

We heard stories ... in Dublin Owen's reputation as a businessman has reached Baile Beag. It is clear that Maire and Bridget are impressed by the stories of his wealth, and look up to him for having become successful. As a merchant in Dublin, however, he must lead a very different lifestyle to that of his family in Baile Beag. He belongs to an anglicised middle class of merchants who benefitted from the expansion of Dublin's commercial ventures, and this is what has evidently brought him into contact with British army officers

Omagh town in county Tyrone, southeast of where the play is set

28 **'civilised'** Owen uses this word ironically in referring to the people of Baile Beag, indicating either that he regards them as uncivilised, or that he is trying to provoke a reaction from them. The word 'civilised' is derived from the Greek for urban settlement, so, strictly speaking, Baile Beag is civilised. Owen may be punning on both meanings of the word

29 **Right, Master** Doalty replies to Hugh's command in a way that is simultaneously deferential and sneering

I'm on their pay-roll Owen's announcement informs the others that he has gone into the service of the British army. To the Donnelly twins, and possibly also to Doalty, this would be regarded as treason

My job ... King's good English Owen is echoing the view of a stereotypical English colonist, here, which may be read as meaning that either Owen has become loyal to English colonial interests in Ireland, or that he is again trying to rile the others

29 **neither a roof ... nor a sod of ground** Maire is chastising Manus for talking of
marriage when he has no house of his own and no land on which to grow
food

30 **aqua vitae** the water of life, which in Gaelic – uisce beatha – refers to
whisky

Nonne Latine ... Gaelic, sir Jimmy is asking in Latin if Lancey knows the
language, and Lancey is made to look stupid as he assumes Jimmy is
speaking to him in Gaelic, which reveals that Lancey knows neither
language

31 **His Majesty ... English mile** Captain Lancey is explaining the project in
which he is involved, which is to make the first detailed ordnance survey
map of Ireland. The project was developed to meet several needs. First, it
was felt that Ireland should benefit from the same comprehensive mapping
as England, to reflect its recent status in the Union of Great Britain and
Ireland (1801). Secondly, the mapping coincided with the valuation of land,
making it possible for taxation to be reassessed. And thirdly, Ireland had
been for centuries under British rule, and in order to sustain this rule, the
British military authorities needed to have accurate and up-to-date
information. In previous centuries, inaccurate and incomplete maps had
made it more difficult for English commanders to conduct effective counter-
rebellion operations

a general triangulation the ordnance survey teams used a technique of
triangulation which had been invented as early as the sixteenth century, but
was applied to Ireland first on a national scale in the ordnance survey of
1826–52. Triangulation meant dividing areas into right-angled triangles. By
measuring the base and three angles, the other sides are calculated
trigonometrically without having to be measured, so minimising the amount
of measuring to be done, and minimising the errors which can be made by
accumulating short, local measuring operations (see Historical Background)

A new map Owen keeps the translation short, and abbreviates Lancey's
statements throughout, altering the meaning of these statements by
removing anything he feels would be interpreted as controversial by local
people. Clearly, the use of the map for reassessing taxation and for military
intelligence would not be greeted favourably

'Ireland ... the interests of Ireland' Lancey is quoting from a statement made
by the Spring Rice committee on 21 June 1824 recommending that
ordnance survey work begin in Ireland and claiming that the mapping of the

entire country could only be taken as proof that the British government had
Ireland's interests in mind

32 **George's task … correct** Owen's hesitation before using the word 'correct'
suggests that he knows there is something sinister about translating the
names, or that he knows the people will be suspicious of it

Has he anything to say? Maire shows an interest in Yolland, the first sign of
something between them

Roland George is obviously friendly with Owen, but the fact that he gets his
name wrong implies that there are serious, unresolved differences between
them yet

What sort of translation … they'll be Anglicised Manus tells Owen that he
knows that Owen was mistranslating Lancey's speech. Owen shows himself
to be slippery here, relying on a defence of ambiguity in poetry to justify his
deliberate falsification of Lancey's words. To Manus, there is no 'ambiguity'
or difficulty with the place-names, and he knows that the agenda of
Lancey's operation is to remove the Gaelic names and replace them with
English ones

33 **It's only a name** Owen reveals his careless attitude to his own name, and to
the place-names he will soon be translating. His argument – 'It's the same
me' – assumes that an object is the same, regardless of its name. This
contrasts with his view later, when he tells his father that he will not be
able to find his way around the local areas now that the place-names have
been changed

Alright … go-between Owen takes on the responsibility not just of
interpreting, but of acting as go-between between the two cultures – British
and Irish. This is, indeed, what he signifies in the play, someone who is
able to straddle both cultures, but who is perhaps out of sorts in both
cultures too

ACT II SCENE 1   **Yolland and Hugh [Owen] argue over place-names and
Maire is attracted to Yolland**

Yolland and Hugh [Owen] are involved principally in filling in the place-names
on to the new maps of the area. It becomes clear that their work is
controversial, because it involves anglicising the Gaelic names. The work
is slow, partly because they are drinking poteen and partly because
Yolland begins to have serious problems with anglicising names which he

has come to love. He and Owen begin to argue about some of the changes to the names. Manus then enters, and announces his news that he has been offered a teaching job on a nearby island. He tells Maire his news as soon as she enters, and seems to propose marriage to Maire, asking her how she would like to live with him on an island. But she hardly notices him, and seems to be distracted by Yolland.

It is clear from the beginning of this scene that Yolland is less than enthusiastic about his role in anglicising place-names. He relishes the Gaelic names, even if he pronounces them poorly. Later, he argues with Owen to preserve the original Gaelic names, and he is depicted falling in love with Baile Beag. For him it represents a different way of life to what he has been accustomed to in England:

I had moved into a consciousness that wasn't striving nor agitated, but at its ease and with its own conviction and assurance. And when I heard Jimmy Jack and your father swopping stories about Apollo and Cuchulainn and Paris and Ferdia – as if they lived down the road – it was then that I thought – I knew – perhaps I could live here … (p. 40)

Yolland is an idealist, who feels sentimental about Baile Beag and romanticises it as 'heavenly'. He stands up for his principles – even when it comes to what seem to others trivial details, such as the name of Tobair Vree. Owen, on the other hand, is a pragmatist, who seems to be indifferent to the fate of the place-names of his homeland, and careless even about whether his own name is pronounced correctly.

The differences between Yolland and Owen in this scene illuminate the debates about the anglicisation of place-names as well as informing us of their character traits. The argument over the name of Tobair Vree, in particular, allows both sides of the case to be presented. Owen argues that the name derives from an event which everybody has forgotten, and so is therefore no longer relevant. Yolland clings to the name because it has a history, even if forgotten. It has sentimental value, if nothing else. Hugh also appears to be a pragmatist when he tells Yolland 'it can happen that a civilisation can be imprisoned in a linguistic contour which no longer matches the landscape of … fact' (p. 43). In a sense, Manus is an idealist in that he refuses to compromise because of Yolland's presence, and continues to speak in Gaelic. It is **ironic**, therefore, at the end of the play that Yolland has disappeared and Manus has run off, while the two pragmatists, Owen and Hugh, have adapted to the changing circumstances around them and have survived.

34 **creel** a wicker basket

reference books church registries, lists of landowners and tenants, grand jury lists, etc. which Owen and Yolland are using to help them decide on place-names for the map

Bun na hAbhann Gaelic place-name, literally, the mouth of the river

35 **Banowen ... Owenmore ... Binhone** Owen and Yolland are finding that previous attempts to record the name of Bun na hAbhann in official documents have not been able to agree

freeholders those who have tenure over land for a guaranteed period for a fee

neither fish nor flesh neither one thing nor the other

Burnfoot the name which was given to the village of Bun na hAbhann which is its name still today. Friel shows Owen conjuring up this name as if from nowhere, but it is actually less absurd than it appears here. Burn is Scottish for a small stream, and foot refers to the point at which it enters the sea. It expresses the same meaning, therefore, as the Gaelic words

George, my name isn't... Owen is about to complain about George calling him 'Roland', but is interrupted

36 **The sappers ... names** the engineers have finished making the map, but Owen and Yolland are lagging behind them in giving names to the places, thereby holding up its printing

Sorry – sorry? Manus has obviously spoken in Gaelic to Yolland, which shows that he is less willing to cooperate with the English soldiers than Manus

your man this man

37 **I understand the Lanceys perfectly...you puzzle me** Manus is suspicious of Yolland who is very friendly with the Irish, whereas Lancey is a familiar figure of English colonial authority. Yolland puzzles Manus because it is less clear whose 'side' Yolland is on, the side whose uniform he is wearing, or the side whose people he seems to be building up a rapport with

37 **there are always the Rolands** 'the Rolands' in this case would mean the people who are willing to betray their own side and desert to help the enemy

Do you know the Donnelly twins? Yolland is asking Owen a question about suspected rebels, and so it is unclear what his motives are. Is he simply curious about who the twins are or is he trying to win some intelligence information from Owen for his superior, Lancey?

38 **addled** confused

Poll na gCaorach hole of the sheep

Baile Beag small town

Ceann Balor the head of Balor (a mythical Irish king)

Lis Maol fort of the dense

Machaire Buidhe yellow plain

Baile na nGall town of the foreigners

Carraig an Ri rock of the king

Mullach Dearg red top or peak

39 **Loch an Iubhair** lake of the yew

capped stopped or fenced in

East India Company a trading company founded in London in 1600 by royal charter to open up British trade in the Far East. It was prevented from extending into the Far East because of Dutch influence, and set up instead in Bengal. The history of the company shows that it worked closely alongside British imperial interest, hence Yolland's father as a colonial administrator would have been able to find his son employment in the company with some ease. The company was dissolved in 1873 following a series of administrative scandals, during which the British government took over responsibility for ruling India from the company

Tra Bhan white beach

40 **Waterloo** the battle of Waterloo, 18 June 1815, near Brussels, in which Napoleon's French forces repeatedly attacked an allied force of British, Dutch, Belgian, German and Prussian troops throughout the day, without success, and retreated from the battlefield. The final battle in the French Revolutionary and Napoleonic Wars (1792–1815), and the end of Napoleon's attempts to dominate Europe

Wellington Arthur Wellesley, 1st Duke of Wellington (1769–1852), soldier and statesman, who commanded the British, Dutch, Belgian and German forces at the battle of Waterloo. He later served as Prime Minister in Britain

40 **Bastille** French revolutionaries captured the state prison of Bastille on 14 July 1789, hoping to find arms. In fact, it was poorly defended and contained a handful of prisoners, with few arms to raid. But it was an important **symbol** of authority as its walls overlooked some of the poorest areas of Paris. The date of the fall of the Bastille, therefore, is celebrated every year in France as a national holiday

the Year One the French revolution, having overthrown the monarchic and aristocratic government in favour of a democratic one, marked the beginning of a new era in French history with a new calendar, beginning in 1793

Apollo Greek and Roman god of intelligence, music, poetry and healing

Cuchulainn (Irish mythology) warrior hero, son of god Lugh, who got his name, the hound of Culainn, when he killed Culainn's fierce guard dog and offered in recompense to guard Culainn's fortress himself. Cuchulainn is chiefly famous for his defence of Ulster against the armies of Queen Medb of Connacht, at which battle he was forced to slay his best friend, Ferdia. When he was dying from battle wounds, he strapped himself to a pillar stone so that he could fight his enemies to the death

Paris (Greek mythology) Paris was rewarded with the most beautiful woman in the world, Helen, for favouring Aphrodite in a disagreement among goddesses. Helen was in love with another suitor, however, and Paris stole her away to Troy, thus sparking off the Trojan war, and fulfilling the prophecy made at his birth that he would be the cause of Troy's ruin

Ferdia Cuchulainn's best friend, who had trained as a warrior with him in Scotland. When the war between Ulster and Connacht broke out, he joined the Connacht army of Queen Medb. He tried to avoid fighting against Cuchulainn, but was tricked into it by Medb. After four days of single combat between them, Cuchulainn slew Ferdia

Poteen ... won't it? Yolland is despairing here of the chances of ever becoming accepted fully in Baile Beag. His lack of knowledge of the Gaelic language is an obvious barrier, but even if he learns it, he feels that there will always be something about the community which will remain secret and elusive from him

41 **Ovid** Publius Ovidius Naso (43BC – AD18), Roman writer of *Metamorphoses*, a narrative of various stories of transformation, in which characters are often transformed into images of their desire. His stories are taken from, or inspired by, a wide range of cultures: Greek poems and myths, Latin folklore, stories from Babylon in the East. The word 'translation' can refer to the transformation of one being or state into another, so this may indicate a significant theme within the play

plebeian uncultured or coarse, although Hugh is probably referring to its use in ancient Rome, meaning of low birth or common

expeditio (Latin) expedition

journeyman tailor a qualified tailor who works for another tailor, therefore living in his shadow, or not able to show off his true talents. It can also mean that the tailor is simply hired from day to day, and has a precarious livelihood

William Wordsworth English Romantic poet (1770–1850), best known for his *Lyrical Ballads* with Samuel T. Coleridge, and *The Prelude*. One of the most famous English poets at the time in which this play is set, so it is incredible that Hugh has not heard of him. The world of Gaelic literature and language was so alien to England that neither culture seemed to be aware of the advances and riches of the other

Wordsworth ... your island Hugh explains that he does not know of English literature, and tells Yolland that his people feel closer to southern than to northern Europe. For the west coast of Ireland, this was largely true: it had trading links with Spain, southern France and even Italy, while it was the east of Ireland which traditionally had links with Scotland, Wales, England and northern France. But it is possible that Hugh is also teasing Yolland, and exaggerating his own ignorance, when he says, dismissively, 'We tend to overlook your island'

42 **We like ... posited** Hugh is suggesting that the people of Gaelic Ireland feel that they live in a timeless world of certainties and 'truths', where nothing changes and the landscape is brimming with the signs of ancient, prehistoric life

Only in Latin, I'm afraid Hugh's modesty reveals that he considers writing in Latin to be less prestigious than writing in Gaelic

A rich language ... spiritual people the Irish people lived in greater poverty than the English, or most of Europe, particularly in the eighteenth and early nineteenth centuries, but they produced a wealth of great literature. Hugh is suggesting that in the face of physical hardship, Irish people turn to less material pursuits, and more to spiritual devotion or literary innovation

No ... find your way? Owen gets tired of his father showing off his intellect to Yolland, and so Owen mocks him by giving him directions using the new anglicised names of the map

42 **Pentaglot Preceptor** teacher of five languages

43 **I understand ... not immortal** Hugh advises Yolland that he should not feel isolated or alienated by a foreign language, such as Gaelic, for languages change and are pliable

it can happen ... fact this is a remarkable statement by Hugh, that a language can cease to reflect the way that the people live. It may indicate that Hugh knows that the Gaelic language is no longer meeting the requirements of its people, as Maire has suggested earlier in the play when she quotes from Daniel O'Connell that the Gaelic language is a 'barrier to modern progress'. Another interpretation, less plausible, perhaps, would be that Hugh is referring to the language of English imperialism as outdated, and failing to keep up with what is actually happening in its colonies

It's an eviction of sorts Yolland recognises that the work that he is doing with Owen does have a sinister aspect, and this has probably come about after he witnessed Owen showing his father that without the familiar Gaelic names, the places around them don't have the same meaning or significance

we're taking place-names ... as we can Owen defends what they are doing by telling Yolland that the Gaelic names are confusing, and that the new names will 'standardise' them. It is unclear to what extent Owen really believes that this is not a sinister exercise, and to what extent he is defending their jobs just for expediency

Tobair Vree from Tobair Bhriain – the well of Brian. The 'bh' is pronounced 'v', and the 'n' became silent over a period of years

44 **So the question ... parish remembers?** Friel's plays frequently contain questions such as this, which communicate the historical choices facing individuals at a particular time. These questions tend not to be answered, which leaves the issue open for debate. In this instance, Yolland and Owen have the choice to change the name, thereby participating in the destruction of Gaelic culture, or to keep the old name, thereby taking a stand against the process of anglicising Ireland. Friel is revealing the extent to which individuals do have some control over their own local destinies, albeit limited and partial

My name is not Roland! Owen finally tells Yolland that he has been calling him by the wrong name since they first met. Yolland must have been unfamiliar with the name 'Owen' and so converted it to something more familiar – 'Roland' – which of course sounds very close to his own name.

Owen's outburst reveals that he isn't quite so uncaring about changing names from their original forms as he pretends to be

45 **We name a thing ... existence** Owen and Yolland are now drunk with the power of inventing and ascribing to places new names. They compare their power to assign names to things and beings with that of Adam in the Garden of Eden, as told in the Book of Genesis. Yolland has just decided to keep the original form of Tobair Vree and Owen has insisted on the genuine form of his name, so their gleeful celebration of the power of inventing new names is **ironic**. But when Manus enters he has no knowledge of this context, and their laughter and boasting about changing the names must seem to him obscene and sinister

46 **speak in English ... colonist?** Manus's response to Owen's request to speak in English shows contempt for Yolland and suspicion of his motives
Inis Meadhon middle island
a rood of standing corn a quarter of an acre of corn
twelve drills of potatoes twelve rows of potatoes
£42 a year a decent salary on which to get married and settle down

47 **How will you like living on an island?** This is Manus's way of asking Maire to marry him, or his way of assuming that she will
We wave to each other across the fields Rather than answering Manus's proposal, Maire seems more interested in Yolland, a sign that she is no longer interested, if she ever was, in a relationship with Manus. This is bound to fuel Manus's resentment of Yolland even further

48 **Fiddler O'Shea's about** This suggests that the musician, a fiddler, is not always about, and presumably is an itinerant who travels from village to village
Tell him then Maire is making sure that Owen tells Yolland about the dance, indicating her interest in him being there
What's he saying ... O for God's sake! a farcical scene in which Owen is left to translate an awkward conversation between Yolland and Maire, who do not speak each other's language
Is your mother at home? Manus wants to talk to Maire's mother, perhaps for the purpose of asking for her daughter's hand in marriage

49 **Bloody, bloody, bloody marvellous!** Yolland is effusive in his love of all things Irish, particularly poteen, it seems

ACT II SCENE 2   Maire and Yolland in love

Maire and Yolland have fallen in love, and this is evident when they emerge from a dance together. At first Maire is shy, and the two find it difficult to communicate as neither speaks the other's language. But Yolland begins to communicate his affection to her by carefully pronouncing the Gaelic place-names which he has come to love. She responds, and together they recite a litany of names which becomes poetic. They caress and express their love for each other. The scene ends with them kissing, while Sarah witnesses them before running off to tell Manus.

The dramatic tension between Maire and Yolland has been building up on stage since Act I. When Yolland first appears in front of the people of Baile Beag, shy and quiet, Maire asks to hear him speak, the first sign that she is interested in him. In Act II, Scene 1, she asks Owen to tell Yolland of the dance. She also tells Owen that they have been waving to each other across the fields. In this scene, they are alone together for the first time, and both are clearly nervous.

In some ways, this is a simple romantic scene, but with an important difference. The lovers do not have a language in common, and so they must attempt to discover a way of communicating their feelings for each other. The solution, after disastrous attempts in Latin and English, is to whisper to each other the Gaelic place-names which Yolland has been employed to change. The poetic recitation of the names is the key which unlocks the intimacy between them. Whereas in the previous scene Yolland has defended keeping the Gaelic names for their sentimental value, an argument which Owen doesn't find very convincing, in this scene he and Maire find the real value of the names – that they are beautiful. This is perhaps because to most audiences the names are in an unknown language and are therefore exotic. Reciting the names in English doesn't have quite the same effect – rivermouth, blackridge, sheepsrock, and so on. But in the final Act, Maire also recites some English place-names which equally are poetic in effect.

49 **Manus'll wonder where I've got to** Maire is showing her embarrassment at being alone with Yolland

The grass ... is soaking Maire and Yolland are speaking in different languages, and they also think in different ways. Maire deduces that the grass is wet because her feet are soaking, whereas Yolland deduces that her feet must be wet because the grass is soaking

50 **The futility of it** both Yolland and Maire attempt to address each other but realise that it is futile. Yolland tries to communicate by speaking English louder and slower, a habit associated stereotypically with the English tourist abroad. Maire speaks to him in broken Latin, a language which he misunderstands as Gaelic

water ... Fire ... Earth Maire recalls three of the four elements from her English lessons. She forgets air

51 **in Norfolk ... first of May** Maire's curious phrase which she has learned from her Aunt Mary, does mean something to Yolland, who begins to tell her about maypole dancing in his mother's home town, before he realises that she can't understand a word

my Aunt Mary ... would she? Maire worries if Yolland's excitement means that the phrase learned from her Aunt was sexually suggestive

Bun na hAbhann ... Lag Maire and Yolland find intimacy by reciting to each other the Gaelic names of local places. Through their mutual love of the place-names they succeed in communicating something of their attractions to each other

52 **'Always'?** Both Maire and Yolland are curious about the word for 'always' in each other's language. There is irony for both, of course, in their failure to recognise the word. 'Always' can mean very little in a community and language which is threatened with extinction, and in their relationship, which turns out to be short-lived

ACT III   Yolland disappears and the play draws towards a tragic climax

Yolland is missing, and more soldiers have arrived to search for him. Some of the characters suspect that the Donnelly twins, local rebels, have something to do with his disappearance. Manus is angry from having found out about Maire and Yolland, and is desperate to get away from Baile Beag. But Lancey's soldiers are already rifling their way through the farms and houses nearby looking for Yolland, and Owen advises Manus not to run away because Lancey might think this a sign of Manus's guilt. But Manus refuses and leaves anyway. Maire arrives but is distraught with the disappearance of Yolland, and she tells them absent-mindedly of the place-names of Yolland's home. Lancey arrives on the scene, and delivers a series of threats to the class through Owen's translations. He threatens evictions, the destruction of livestock and crops, and the levelling of every house in the area. But resistance to the army's threats has already started, as Doalty notices that the army's camp is on fire.

The play concludes with Hugh facing unemployment as he is told that he will not be headmaster at the national school, with Maire lost and confused, and even more desperate to learn English, with Jimmy Jack still wrapped up in the classics, and with Doalty, Bridget and Owen all running after the soldiers, either to resist them or to stop the mayhem caused by them. *Translations* reaches its tragic climax. Bridget smells the sweet scent of rotting potato stalks in the air, a prophetic sign of potato famine. Hugh delivers the final speech of the play, in which he tries to recite Virgil's description of how Carthage was destroyed by the Romans, but somehow Hugh cannot remember all the words.

Although there are tensions between the characters in the preceding scenes, relationships between the characters are stable and, for the most part, amicable, until the turbulent and tragic climax in this final Act. Whereas Doalty shows kindness to Yolland earlier in the play, here he feels compelled to respond violently to the actions of the other English soldiers. Manus too feels that he has to resort to desperate measures. Friel is showing us individuals who are drawn into action by changing circumstances. In this case, the event which has precipitated a crisis – the disappearance of Yolland – is outside the control of any of the characters. The relationships between Yolland and Owen, and Yolland and Maire, have suggested that Irish and English people, although they have different cultural traditions and social customs, may live together harmoniously. The tragedy of this final Act is that events beyond these characters' control prevent them from so doing.

The fragility of human relationships is the subject of this final Act. The love between Maire and Yolland was bound to be difficult, given the barriers in language and culture, but their relationship is destroyed by the political antagonisms between the English army and Irish rebels. Manus is consumed with jealousy of Yolland's relationship with Maire, and can only respond pathetically with 'the wrong gesture in the wrong language'. Jimmy Jack breaks down in tears, abandoning the pretences of living in his mythical world, and crying to Hugh of the need for companionship. Hugh also is made pathetic by circumstance, knocked from his perch of pomposity and self-conceit, and left unemployed by the new national school. His memory fades, and his final lines suggest that his world is on the brink of destruction.

54 **limekiln** a kiln for heating limestone
Murren in English, the murrain refers to a plague, or infectious blight. It is significant in this scene because Bridget later smells in the air the first signs of potato blight, which caused numerous famines in early nineteenth-century Ireland, including the Great Famine of 1845–50, which decimated the Irish population, and almost wiped out the Gaelic-speaking areas of western Ireland. In Irish, Murren derives from Saint Muranus

55 **Those ... to go** Manus is desperate to get out of Baile Beag, and to delay taking up his new job in Inis Meadhon, but it is not clear why. He is obviously upset by what Sarah has told him about Maire and Yolland, and perhaps he needs time to think about his feelings and his future
Clear out ... involved somehow: Owen tells Manus that running away will be understood by Captain Lancey as a sign of guilt. This is the first hint that something is wrong in Baile Beag
You know George Yolland has gone missing, and the army are out searching for him. The disappearance of an army officer, even one involved only in map-making, is a serious matter in a country in which the army knows about the existence of rebels, such as the Donnelly twins. Now it is clear that Manus's departure may be taken by Lancey as a sign that he has been involved in Yolland's disappearance, and after what Sarah has told him about Maire and Yolland, Manus has a plausible motive for harming Yolland
The lame scholar turned violent: Manus is struck by how pathetic he must have seemed with his lame leg, struggling to find Yolland to strike him with a stone

55 **The wrong gesture in the wrong language:** Manus has not harmed Yolland. He tells Owen that he hurled only an insult at Yolland, who, in any case, didn't understand it because it was in Gaelic. Manus feels that he would have been better to have insulted him in English, at least then Yolland would have understood that it was an act of defiance, rather than an attempt to communicate with him. Manus says that this was 'the wrong gesture in the wrong language', and this echoes his earlier statement that Doalty's trick with the surveyor's pole was 'a gesture ... to indicate a presence' (p. 18). Manus has learned now that some gestures are better than others, that gestures, in order to be effective, must be understood

56 **Tell father ... those things** Manus is leaving, taking three books with him, by Virgil, Caesar and Aeschylus, which he sold his pet lamb to buy – which signifies how valuable they are to him. Owen seems to be taking on the responsibility of looking after Hugh here, for Manus implies by his instructions that Hugh is not able to fend for himself and Owen seems to be accepting his instructions

MANUS ... **Sarah** A similar scene to the one in Act I, in which Manus is coaching Sarah to speak properly. Manus is colder towards Sarah now, and seems to interrogate her for her answers rather than help her with her words. His lack of warmth conveys the anger which he is feeling, but she takes it to mean that she has done something wrong and begins to cry

57 **I'm sorry ...** Sarah is apologising to Manus for having brought the bad news of Maire and Yolland, but Manus has already left

SARAH *nods* Now that Manus has gone, Sarah is no longer speaking and has regressed to communicating in signs and nods

Fifty more soldiers ... Cnoc na nGabhar Although Doalty is excited by the news that he brings, the arrival of the soldiers is sinister, for they are already beginning to destroy crops and stores in their search for Yolland. The earlier romanticism of the play has now gone. Yolland may have been sentimental about Ireland, and may have fallen in love with an Irish woman and Irish place-names, but he was also an officer in the English army. The soldiers are demonstrating their power to destroy as a reminder of what military presence represents

58 **Visigoths ...** *Rustici*: Jimmy Jack shouts at the soldiers some reminders of barbarous warrior peoples who acted in similarly destructive ways when they were conquering other places. Visigoths and Vandals were Germanic and the Huns were Asian peoples who invaded former territories of the Roman

empire in the fourth and fifth centuries AD. The Visigoths even sacked Rome itself in AD410, so marking them out as destroyers of civilisation. He then calls them names in Latin: ignoramus, fools, peasants. Jimmy Jack is either making an astute and **ironic** parallel between English soldiers destroying Irish land and barbaric tribes sacking Rome, or he is demonstrating once again that he is trapped in the myths of the past even when soldiers are upsetting his homeland

Thermopylae the site of a famous battle in 480BC where a small army of Spartans were defeated by invading hordes of Persian warriors. It is a narrow pass between mountains and sea, linking Locris and Thessaly

Mayo, maybe Manus has probably set out to go south and further west, into Mayo, but even Owen doesn't know if this is his real destination

Leave me … the Donnelly twins Bridget lets slip that she knows something about what happened to Yolland, as she knows enough to point to the Donnelly twins

59 **'I'll see you yesterday'** Maire recalls Yolland's last words to her, as he attempted to speak Gaelic but got 'yesterday' confused with 'tomorrow'. This error is revealing, as it conveys the impression that there are no certainties, no tomorrows, just as Maire and Yolland were confused by the word 'always'. In Yolland's confusion of tenses, future with past, he echoes the theme of being trapped in the past

60 **Come here … his Homer** Maire recites the names of Yolland's homeland, pronouncing them as both she and Yolland did with Gaelic names the night before. The place-names become like poetry, like Jimmy Jack's Homer

I hope … Brooklyn Maire is indicating that she has nothing left to do but to embark for America, for Brooklyn in New York

61 **like bloody beagles** Doalty is referring to the soldiers, who will chase Manus like hunting dogs, now that he is under suspicion

LANCEY **… *the commanding officer*** Lancey may have appeared earlier as a harmless, stiff-upper-lipped officer, in charge of a map-making expedition, but he becomes in this scene a ruthless commander, determined to punish the whole community because someone has harmed or hidden Yolland

this section It may be a village or townland to the people, but to Lancey Baile Beag is a square on a map, a military 'section'

O'Donnell Lancey is strict with Owen, addressing him by his surname

61–2 **Lieutenant Yolland … got to do** In contrast to Owen's translation of Lancey's speech in Act I, Owen translates accurately here. Lancey is threatening the local people that if Yolland isn't found, or if no information is forthcoming about his whereabouts, the army will kill their livestock and evict them from their houses. Owen is also forced to translate the anglicised names which he has given to the local places back into Gaelic

62 **a wake** the play begins with a christening, and now is coming to an end with a wake, the mourning of the dead

his whole camp's on fire Doalty notices that the army camp is on fire, perhaps the first sign of rebellion

63 **We'll ... beasts somewhere** ... to prevent the soldiers from killing them

God ... destroyed altogether Bridget is relieved that the smell is just the fire at the army camp and not rotting potatoes. Famine is obviously a much more serious threat to her than anything the army can do

When my grandfather ... without a fight Doalty knows that there are precedents for the army's actions, and the people of Baile Beag have survived such threats and acts of violence before. He is also certain that he will use violence to resist them

64 **The Donnelly twins know how** know the answer as to how to resist the army. Their use of guerrilla war tactics means that they can strike at the army fast and when they least expect it, and then disappear so that they don't get caught. What Doalty doesn't see is that the Donnelly twins have also deserted the people of Baile Beag, and left them to suffer the violent backlash from the army

Bartley Timlin Timlin has been appointed to the job as schoolmaster which Hugh told his pupils earlier was promised to him

'I am a barbarian ... anyone' which suggests that barbarians are always defined by the people to whom they are strangers. Barbarian doesn't necessarily mean that they are lacking in culture or intelligence, but means simply that their values are not shared by other tribes or races

65 **Athene** the Greek goddess. It may be that Jimmy is about to marry someone local but describes her comically as his Athene. **Metis from Hellespont** was the wife of Jupiter (**Zeus**) who was eaten by him when Jupiter feared that she would bear a child more cunning than him. When Vulcan opened up Jupiter's head, **Pallas Athene** was born. Given that Jimmy breaks down in tears and cannot continue to tell Hugh of Athene, it is more likely that this is one of Jimmy Jack's stories, to compensate for his loneliness, borrowed from his world of myths

66 **We must learn ... our new home:** Whereas Doalty is planning to resist the
English army when they come to evict him, Hugh is planning to comply with
what the army want, hoping to appease the new order in Baile Beag by
learning the new English names

it is not ... language facts of history are not important, merely what comes
to us from the past through language. Words, as Hugh has taught his pupils
throughout the play, contain in them the history of the roots of a civilisation

we must never ... fossilise when we remain trapped in language which, in a
phrase which Hugh has used earlier, 'no longer matches the landscape of
fact', we have to reinvigorate that language

Edictum imperatoris the imperial verdict – even when Owen is trying to
convince Hugh that this is not some mythological tale but the real threat of
violence which is facing them, Hugh responds in Latin, speaking of the
Roman empire

67 **To remember ... madness** see George Steiner's *After Babel*: 'To remember
everything is a condition of madness. We remember culturally, as we do
individually, by conventions of emphasis, foreshortening, and omission'
(p. 29). In the last lines of the play, Hugh cannot remember fully a passage
from Virgil which he once knew well, hence emphasising the limitations of
memory. As he is trying to remember the prophecy of the destruction of a
civilisation, the Carthaginians, it is significant that his memory begins to
fail him at this point

1798 the 1798 rebellion in Ireland was organised by a Republican
organisation, the United Irishmen, inspired and supported by French
revolutionaries. They fought against the English army in Wexford,
Antrim, and Mayo chiefly, but were disorganised and inadequately
armed, and were defeated in the summer of that year. Jimmy and Hugh
were young men, going off to fight with the rebels, fired with enthusiasm
and a romantic idealism inspired by Virgil's *Aeneid*. They did not make it
very far, however, deciding to turn back after twenty-three miles. But they
manage to make even their cowardice sound heroic, by describing
themselves as Ulysses, 'homesick for Athens'

I will teach you English Hugh has been reluctant to teach Maire English
before, but now he recognises that English is part of the new reality of their
lives

'always' Hugh dismisses the word 'always' as 'silly', and given that
the world around him is under threat, and faces a new language

and culture, the concept of permanence cannot be anything but
ridiculous

68 **Do you know ... about that** Jimmy Jack indicates the difficulty with the
relationship between Maire and Yolland, that it crossed tribal barriers. It
was bound to cause trouble in both 'tribes'. There is a hint here that
Yolland has been harmed in some way because he crossed those barriers.
But Jimmy Jack turns out not to be commenting on the relationship
between Maire and Yolland, but on the relationship between the goddess
Athene and himself

***Urbs antiqua fuit ...* Lybia's downfall** Hugh tries to remember the opening of
Virgil's *Aeneid*, but he cannot remember it fully and has to recite it again.
The passage he is quoting is the prophecy of the destruction of Carthage by
the Romans. Carthage was a city on the north African coast, which Virgil
tells us was loved by the Roman goddess Juno who believed it would be
capital of all nations. But she then foresaw that there would arise a Roman
empire from the blood of Aeneas, which would one day conquer the
Carthaginians and sack their city. Hugh is, perhaps, thinking of a parallel
between the destruction of Baile Beag by the English and the destruction of
Carthage by the Romans. The **irony** of Virgil's *Aeneid* is that it contains the
prophecy of Carthage's tragic destruction but is written in the language of
those who destroyed it. *Translations* contains the story of the tragic
destruction of Gaelic culture, and it also is written in the language of those
who destroyed it

ΞAL APPROACHES

CHARACTERISATION

REPRESENTATIVE' CHARACTERS

The characters in *Translations* are all, in some way, charismatic and believable. Each has her or his own particular traits and habits, and the play contains some very skilful and entertaining characters, including Hugh, Jimmy Jack, Doalty, Yolland and Maire. Their qualities are constructed through dress, dialogue and action, sometimes in the simplest of gestures. They are also, however, in some way, representative of particular views and beliefs. All the characters represent different aspects of the same political process – the transformation of an antiquated Gaelic society into a modern British colony.

Lancey and Yolland represent the English officials and soldiers who administer and police the changes. They also **symbolise** different attitudes among the English colonisers: some who regard Ireland without any emotion whatsoever (Lancey), and others who sentimentalise Ireland as an exotic and romantic place (Yolland). The Donnelly twins, whom we never see, represent those who are opposed violently to British rule in Ireland. Manus, Doalty and Bridget seem to represent people who are sympathetic towards violent resistance to British rule, but who become involved directly themselves only when they are forced by circumstance. Initially, Owen is the interpreter between the soldiers and the people, who seems to border on being a traitor, but towards the end of the play he appears to regret having played this role. Hugh and Jimmy Jack are symbolic of the mindset trapped in romanticising the past and oblivious partly to the events of the present. Hugh is also like Yolland and Maire, however, in symbolising the capacity to open one's mind and heart to other cultures and lifestyles. The love between Yolland and Maire, even if it is doomed to fail, represents the possibility for peace between two nations or cultures by their willingness to learn about and love one another's values and customs.

Broadly speaking, then, these characters represent a spectrum of possible political positions and ideals which might be as useful in the context of Ireland in 1980 as they are of Ireland in 1833. It is the relationships between these characters, and the various positions which they adopt in relation to each other, that produce the tensions and movement of the play. Manus's response to the fledgling relationship between Maire and Yolland is part of the tension of the play's final half, while the knowledge that Hugh's life as a schoolmaster and a scholar might be drawing to a tragic end fuels the audience's suspense. The tension of the play comes from its human relationships rather than from its action. For example, much more could have been made of Yolland's disappearance to build up the audience's interest, whereas we do not even find out what happens to Yolland. This could be a criticism of the play, or it might indicate that Friel is directing our attention not to the single individual acts of violence but to the wider set of human relationships.

THE ENGLISH STEREOTYPE

English drama in the eighteenth century frequently utilised the stage-Irishman as a comic device, displaying a propensity for **malapropisms**, nonsensical thought, heavy drinking and quarrelsomeness. His weaknesses and perverse logic served to confirm and congratulate English audiences for their sense, rationality and civilised manners. In Irish drama of the twentieth century a number of playwrights have sought to dispel the stage-Irishman, most notably George Bernard Shaw in *John Bull's Other Island*, which features a stage-Irishman who is revealed to be a Glaswegian and who plays up the stage-Irish image to make money from English audiences. There also developed in Irish drama the stage-Englishman as a counter to the stage-Irishman. The stage-Englishman took two forms, both of which are found in Friel's *Translations*. The first is the Englishman who is cold, superrational and reserved, but who is capable of great brutality. Captain Lancey represents this figure in *Translations*. The second is the Englishman who is an enthusiastic devotee of anything Irish, and who becomes a figure of fun for Irish audiences because he refuses to acknowledge any of the realities or difficulties of life in Ireland. Lieutenant Yolland is such a figure in Friel's play. He decides that he would like to stay in Ireland because 'it's really heavenly', and cries out on drinking poteen that it is 'bloody, bloody, bloody marvellous!'.

CONVERTS OR TRADUCERS?

Lancey and the Donnelly twins are on opposite extremes of the political spectrum, and seem to be determined in getting their way through the use of physical force. But there are a number of characters in *Translations* who are willing to embrace other cultures and beliefs. Owen is an early example in the play when he arrives with the English soldiers as their interpreter, and he is an enthusiastic participant in the job of anglicising the place-names of his homeland. Hugh, towards the play's end, resigns himself to the inevitability of English becoming the language of the people, and of Gaelic culture declining in importance. Maire and Yolland are perhaps the play's best examples of characters who are willing to give up the customs, language and beliefs in which they have been brought up, to convert to an alternative culture. The play is ambiguous as to how we are to interpret and identify these characters however. Are they converts, to be admired for their capacity to embrace another culture? Or are they traducers, who abandon the love and warmth of their own culture and betray it to another?

Yolland, for example, in his enthusiasm for all things Irish, does not contradict or dispute any of Hugh's slanderous criticisms of English culture, and seems to give up any loyalty he might have had to his home. And yet he has enough love for his homeland to describe in intimate detail to Maire its landscape and place-names. So too, Owen is willing to abandon names and customs which have been part of his family's and his community's history and culture for centuries, but shows in his own story of the name of 'Tobair Vree' that he has an intimate knowledge of that history and culture. The issue of whether these characters are converts or traducers is particularly important with the Irish characters. It may be possible that Owen, Maire, and Hugh are the realists in the play who are willing to compromise parts of their own culture in order to gain peace and reconciliation with those from other cultures. It is equally possible that they are the vandals in the play, whose weakness in failing to defend their own culture results in its destruction and slander.

Alienation

Almost all the characters appear to experience **alienation** in some way.
Lancey is alienated as a foreigner in a country for which he appears to
have no affection or understanding. Yolland tells Hugh that he feels cut
off from the people and he is frustrated by being unable to communicate
freely with them. Owen displays some feelings of alienation from Baile
Beag on his return. He is dressed differently and does not seem to fit in
with life in Baile Beag any more. One might ask of the other characters
if they feel comfortable and at home in Baile Beag, particularly as many
of them seem to be pursuing means of escape. Maire is desperate to
emigrate from the village. Jimmy Jack escapes from whatever feelings of
loneliness he might have through his classical poetry. Hugh escapes
through drinking heavily and by entertaining several myths and images of
himself which are exaggerated.

The act of translating Gaelic names into English might be
interpreted as an attempt by the English characters to feel more
comfortable in Ireland, by making the names less foreign and strange to
them. But, if this is so, it succeeds in estranging the local people from
their own homes. Hugh is asked by Owen if he will be able to find his
way around his own locality now that the names have changed, and Maire
sets out for somewhere towards the end of the play but gets lost and
returns. These are signs that the local people have been alienated from
their own community.

Translation

The theme of translation is prevalent throughout the play. Hugh
constantly asks his pupils to translate from Greek or Latin into Irish.
Jimmy Jack translates from Greek into Irish. Owen translates Lancey's
English into Irish, and translates Irish place-names into English for
Yolland. These are examples of linguistic translation. But Friel was
influenced by George Steiner's argument that all language and all
communication are forms of translation. The map which Lancey and
Yolland are making, for example, is a translation of landscape on to
paper. The book which Hugh tells Yolland he is writing is a translation
of school lessons into a textbook. There are other examples of translation

as interpretation. When Owen translates Lancey's announcements in Act I, he changes the meanings of what Lancey says, and makes them less suspect to the people of Baile Beag. Yolland calls Owen 'Roland' which is an interesting translation of 'Owen', which Yolland either misheard or could not pronounce properly, into a sound which is very like 'Yolland'. This suggests that translation is always an act of making something which is strange sound more familiar and comfortable to us. The theme of baptism, which translates a person or thing into a named identity, appears several times in the play also. Steiner argued that language exists to communicate and to conceal, and that distinct languages were formed out of the need for privacy. Language could be used, therefore, to define a tribe or people by a common set of codes for communication, but it could also be used to exclude those who did not belong to the tribe. The conversion of a people from one language to another, as it takes place in Friel's play, suggests that the people are being integrated with another tribe so that they can have no privacies or intimacies of their own.

FAILURE OF COMMUNICATION

In many ways, *Translations* is a pessimistic play, particularly about the capacity of people from different cultures to communicate to each other. There are clearly several major differences between the Irish and English characters in the language they speak, the values they cherish and the cultural beliefs they hold. It is possible for them to resolve their differences, or at least to ignore their differences, by celebrating what they love about each other's culture, as Maire and Yolland do. But both sides fail to express themselves, or their real feelings, to each other, and they resort instead to violence and destruction, as we know is particularly the case with Lancey and the Donnelly twins. This situation, of violence as a sign of the failure to communicate in language, obviously has resonances for the situation in Northern Ireland in 1980, when the possibility of peaceful discussions between the Irish nationalists and the British government seemed to be very far away.

There are several other examples in the play of the failure of communication more generally. Yolland fails to understand what several characters say to him. Owen doesn't communicate his feelings fully to Yolland. Manus doesn't express his feelings fully to Maire. Manus makes 'the wrong gesture in the wrong language' (p. 55). The play is rife with such incidents in which characters fail to make themselves understood, and fail to understand what is being said to them. *Translations* is highlighting the importance of language, and communication in general, for the conflicts between different groups of people. Friel argued that language was particularly significant in Northern Ireland: 'I think that is how the political problem of this island is going to be solved. It's going to be solved by the recognition of what language means for us on this island. Because we are in fact talking about accommodation or marrying of two cultures here, which are ostensibly speaking the same language but which in fact aren't' (Richtarik, *Acting Between the Lines*, 1994, p. 35). The idea that two groups of people can be 'ostensibly speaking the same language' while in fact speaking two very different languages is a key to understanding why Friel has presented both communities (Irish and English) speaking through the medium of English. It allows him to show his audience that the two sets of characters are saying very different things.

IRELAND: LAND OF SAINTS AND SCHOLARS?

There are not many saints in *Translations*, but the play does confirm the myth that Ireland was a land of great learning and scholarship. There has been debate about the accuracy of the play in suggesting that the hedge-schools of Ireland were havens of classical scholars, with some historians disputing the suggestion that the hedge-schools taught anything more than elementary skills of arithmetic, writing and reading. Most of the pupils appear, however successfully, to be in the process of learning Greek or Latin, and Hugh, Manus and Jimmy Jack obviously have a command of several languages. Hugh, for example, knows four languages, is a poet in Gaelic, and purports to be writing textbooks for instructing students in five languages. Furthermore, the classical learning of the local people seems to be embedded in their way of life. Jimmy Jack uses Virgil for advice on agriculture, for example, and both he and Hugh make constant parallels between the English colonisation of Ireland and the Roman imperial conquests. Hugh contends that Gaelic language and literature are rooted in the classical learning of Europe, whereas he treats English literature as a minor provincial genre.

THEMES continued

ENGLISH UPSTARTS

Hugh in particular presents Gaelic culture as an ancient set of honourable traditions and customs which are dignified and civilised, and he contrasts it with English culture, which he thinks is base and materialistic. The Gaelic chieftains, from one family of whom – the O'Donnell chieftains – Hugh is descended, often viewed the English invaders and colonisers as upstarts who had no noble blood in their veins and no culture of learning or civilisation. Hugh's criticism of the English language, that it is particularly suited to commerce, is characteristic of the attitude which the Gaelic nobles expressed about the English in the sixteenth and seventeenth centuries. The English colonisers in Ireland seemed to be more interested in the pursuit of money and power than in nobler spiritual and intellectual endeavours. Of course, Hugh's criticisms of the English are **ironic**, because he has material and commercial needs as much as any Englishman. Lancey and Yolland are depicted as having no classical learning, and so they appear to be rather weak intellectually, but this is hardly likely to have been the case for English military officers at this time. There are, therefore, a few myths purveyed in the play about the differences between the noble Irish and the base English.

DRAMATIC TECHNIQUES

STRUCTURE

The play's story is tightly constructed. It begins by introducing to the audience the situation. A village community in Ireland, whose eccentric characters gather in the hedge-school, is to be mapped and its place-names 'standardised' for the map. English soldiers are to carry out this task. Act I defines the characters and explores some of the relationships between them, including the relationship between Owen and Manus, between Hugh and Jimmy Jack, and between Manus and Maire. The situation is then complicated as some of the implications of this project become more apparent. The standardising of the place-names will mean that the linguistic and cultural traditions of the Irish community will be compromised and even destroyed. The mapping and renaming exercise now begins to appear threatening. One of the English soldiers, Yolland, is unhappy with the project, and he comes to love the community, and particularly one of its inhabitants, Maire. There are also strong tensions between the characters which will be exposed further in the final Act. Manus is clearly jealous of the relationship between Yolland and Maire. Hugh is already hinting that the world around him is about to be transformed, and suggests that this doesn't really surprise him. These complications now move swiftly towards a tense and tragic conclusion. Yolland goes missing, feared killed by local rebels. The army react violently to his disappearance and begin to destroy crops, fences and livestock. The rebels respond with more violence, and an air of uncertainty and fear hangs over the villagers. At the conclusion of the play their whole way of life looks as if it may be coming to an end.

The structure of *Translations* allows Friel to explore several layers of events and themes. On one level, it is about a series of local incidents in a small village in northwest Ireland in 1833, which compel the characters to change the ways in which they live. On another level, it is about the theme of cross-cultural conflict and communication, about whether or not any two groups of people, anywhere in the world, can exist together harmoniously, especially when one group is dominated by the other. The play can be read or performed for its political messages, its human concerns, its dramatic qualities, its historical interests, or, indeed for all these matters. In a simple setting, with a relatively small cast of characters, *Translations* has managed to represent a wide gamut of themes and interests.

LANGUAGE AND TRANSLATION

Translations presents two groups of people with different languages. The English soldiers arrive without any knowledge of Gaelic, and most of the Irish inhabitants of Baile Beag do not have any knowledge of English. Friel is interested in exploring the difficulties of how these two groups of people communicate with one another, but the problem is that not many of his audiences will have knowledge of Gaelic. Both Irish and English characters are therefore represented through the English language. The audiences are informed early in the play that they are to believe that the Irish characters are speaking in Gaelic:

MAIRE: That's the height of my Latin. Fit me better if I had even that much English.

JIMMY: English? I thought you had some English?

MAIRE: Three words. (p. 15)

Friel uses a number of ways of reminding his audiences that Gaelic is being spoken. The Irish characters sometimes talk about not knowing any English. The English characters sometimes show that they are unable to understand what is being spoken by the Irish characters. The Irish characters are also differentiated from the English ones in their speech patterns, with **Hiberno-English** grammar, for example, and in their dress and names. This device of presenting two languages through the medium of one is a crucial component of the play since it enables Friel to present us with two communities who are alienated from each other by a language barrier, without alienating the audiences from the play by that same language barrier, and it reflects the fact that most Irish audiences today do not speak Gaelic.

THE ENDING

One of the most conventional structures for a play is to begin with a situation, then introduce some complications, before moving towards a resolution. As outlined in the section on 'Structure' above, Friel's *Translations* follows this convention in the first two Acts, but in Act III he avoids resolving the situation. Yolland is missing, and we do not find out what has happened to him. Maire wants to leave, but we do not know if she will ever emigrate. Hugh ends the play in confusion, unable to remember a passage from Virgil which he once used to know. There appear to be lots of 'loose ends' in the play, lots of uncertainties which are unresolved. The play ends at the very point at which the community which we have been watching or reading about may be destroyed by the army, but we do not find out what happens to it. We might think that this is a weakness in the play. But there might be reasons for these loose ends. Given what we know about the Donnelly twins, and what they represent historically, it is most likely that Yolland has been killed. Given what we know about emigration around this time, it is likely that Maire did emigrate. And given what we know about English army actions in Ireland, it is likely that the community was damaged in some way, and some people may even have been killed. The play might be depending on our impressions or knowledge of Irish history to fill in some of the blanks. Hugh's confusion is quite appropriate at the conclusion to the play, as Hugh has told Jimmy just a few minutes beforehand that 'confusion is not an ignoble condition' (p. 67). If we are confused at the end of the play, then, it may be because Friel is attempting to convey to his audience the uncertainty and confusion which were the result for Irish people of the events depicted in the play, and leaving the audience free to make their own judgements about those events.

LANGUAGE AND STYLE

CLASS AND EDUCATION

There are differences between the language used by the characters in *Translations* which can be attributed to their social class or level of education. Hugh and Lancey, for example, are both highly articulate in their speech, and have more in common in the way they speak than Hugh and Doalty. Some productions have made a feature out of this. The 1996 revival of *Translations* at the Abbey Theatre in Dublin had Hugh speaking in an English accent. As a more anglicised accent has often been taken as a sign of higher social class in Ireland, this conveyed the sense that Hugh differed from most of his pupils in terms of class identity. Manus and Owen also differ in their speech, with Manus speaking in more local tones, using **colloquialisms**, for example, whereas Owen, coming from his life as 'a city gent' in Dublin, adopts a pompous (even if **ironic**) tone: 'My job is to translate the quaint, archaic tongue you people persist in speaking into the King's good English' (p. 29). Even the fact that Hugh, Manus and Owen know the English language marks them out as being of a higher class than Doalty, Maire and Bridget.

GEORGE STEINER

Friel was inspired by many of George Steiner's arguments in *After Babel* about language and translation. Steiner argued, for instance, that when languages disappeared, the identities of the communities which used them tended to dissolve too. With the death of a language, a whole way of thinking, living and acting died too: 'Each takes with it a storehouse of consciousness' (Steiner, 1975, p. 54). Friel was evidently moved by the implication that with the decline of the Gaelic language in the nineteenth century went a whole chunk of Irish culture and society. Steiner also argued that languages died out not because of any inherent weakness in the language, but because the language was not in touch with the 'principal currents of intellectual and political force. Countless tribal societies have withered inward, isolated by language barriers even from their near neighbours' (p. 56). The fact that Hugh claims never to have heard of Wordsworth is a sign that his language and culture have failed to keep up with the modern world, even the major events and trends of their nearest neighbour. Their only source of inspiration appears to be ancient Greek and Latin, which means that they have no contact with other living cultures and languages. Steiner's book had a lot to say about the untranslatability of one language to another. Something always gets lost in translation, because there is no absolute equivalence between languages. It is, therefore, impossible to escape from misunderstanding and confusion in the translation of one language into another, and Steiner made it clear that translation occurred within languages as much as between languages. We translate complex words into simple ones, unfamiliar phrases into familiar ones, and in the process we cannot avoid changing the meaning of words and phrases, however slightly. Steiner argued therefore that 'true understanding is possible only when there is silence' (p. 286), which is the only 'language' which cannot be mistranslated. Sarah is obviously an important reminder of this argument in *Translations*.

TEXTUAL ANALYSIS

Sadly it is not possible to reproduce the passages in question within this Note. You will need to refer to your own copy of the play when reading the analyses.

Three passages have been selected from *Translations* to illustrate different aspects of the play, such as language and style, characterisation, staging and performance issues, and recurrent themes and techniques. After an initial indication of the significance of each piece of text, the information will then be given in note form so that you can be guided by suggestions, rather than influenced by essays which espouse a particular point of view.

TEXT 1   (from **ACT I PAGES 24–25**; *from* HUGH: Before we commence… *to* MAIRE: I'm talking about…)

This scene occurs shortly after Hugh, the school master, has returned from a baptism at which he has had a few drinks, and begins to teach his class of pupils. He is teaching some of them the Classics and others how to do arithmetic, but much of his teaching consists of passing on local news to them. The significance of this scene is that it informs us of the imminent arrival of Captain Lancey of the Royal Engineers, and it highlights the controversies surrounding the language issue in the play, by showing us that the characters differ in their attitudes to the English language, in particular.

CHARACTERS
Hugh is clearly shown to be in authority. He controls the class by interspersing the information which he wants to impart to them with questions which test their abilities in Latin vocabulary and grammar. He also dismisses them quickly for not knowing answers, as he does with Maire when he asks for the Latin for 'acquiesced', and is impatient with pupils who interrupt him or ask awkward questions – 'Well, girl?'. He is

opinionated and self-assured. He spurns one of the most renowned and admired Irish politicians of his time, Daniel O'Connell, by describing him as 'that little Kerry politician', and he makes confident statements as if they were self-evident truths: 'English ... couldn't really express us'. He is preoccupied with his own importance, so much that he shows no interest in major figures such as Daniel O'Connell and William Wordsworth. He also seems only to admire in other people their willingness to agree with him: 'to his credit he acquiesced to my logic'. And he is insensitive to the reactions and feelings of others. The stage directions indicate that he fails to notice how he has hurt Maire with his comments on the English language, and he appears to be unaware of the **irony** of repudiating English as the language of commerce while he shouts for a slice of bread from Manus.

Maire wants to learn the English language, and this leads her into an argument with her school master, who voices his distaste for English as a language of 'commerce'. She indicates her disagreement with him first by turning away and remaining silent when he asks a question, and then by interrupting him and challenging his authority. She shows herself to be sufficiently self-confident to take a stand against the authority of the master, although the stage directions tell us that she does this 'uneasily but determinedly'. She is an idealist and a fighter, who is willing to stand up for what she wants. She differs from Doalty and Bridget in that she knows the answers to Hugh's questions, and, rather than knowing gossip about Daniel O'Connell's sexual exploits and his 'scrounging' for votes, she is able to quote from his speeches. She is aware that English will be of better use to her than Greek or Latin, and represents the will to embrace **modernity** as opposed to the master's clinging to **antiquity**.

Doalty is shown in this scene to be bright and alert, although just before this Hugh has told him that he knows nothing. It is rare for Doalty to know an answer to one of the master's questions, and here he surprises even himself by being able to answer correctly Hugh's question about the meaning of 'conjugation'. He is also aware of the gossip surrounding the politician, Daniel O'Connell. He points out to his fellow pupils that, although O'Connell talks about the necessity of Irish people learning the English language, O'Connell uses the Irish language to get his votes. Doalty is shown here to be bright, then, but also a joker, prodding and winking at Bridget. He may be prodding and winking at her because of the meaning of the word 'conjugate', which can refer to wedding rituals.

Bridget, like Doalty, is a minor character, and is a fair student, but seems to be more interested in what is going on outside class than inside it. She knows the gossip about Daniel O'Connell, too, but she is also conscientious enough to know her Latin grammar. Thus, unlike Doalty, there is no surprise when Bridget knows the answer to the master's questions.

Jimmy Jack is notably docile through this extract, answering the occasional question, until Bridget mentions the sexual activities of Daniel O'Connell. Jimmy is suddenly awake and interested in any mention of sex or women, and throughout the play Jimmy is obsessed with marrying a goddess.

Although Manus is offstage during this part of the play, we learn that Manus is mistreated by Hugh, who shouts orders at him and speaks to his own son as if he was his personal slave.

RECURRENT THEMES AND TECHNIQUES

Language is a persistent concern of the play, obviously, and in this scene we see Maire arguing with Hugh that it is the English language which the pupils need to be taught. Hugh teaches them the classical languages of Latin and Greek, while Maire demands to learn English. The difference between them is that Hugh believes that knowing the classical languages is worth while because it cultivates their learning, whereas Maire's approach to education is much more utilitarian. Languages for her are only worth learning when they have a practical purpose in life. Gaelic is also marked out as a language with no practical purpose, and Maire cites O'Connell's argument that Gaelic was hindering Ireland from becoming a modern, industrialised and commercial nation. Hugh contends that Gaelic is the essence of who the Irish people are, and that English couldn't express Irishness. The issue for Maire, however, is that English will help her to advance in life and give her better opportunities, whereas Gaelic will entrap her in impoverished, rural Ireland.

Cultural differences between the English and the Irish, and among the Irish themselves, are suggested in this extract. Hugh represents the

English Captain Lancey as a humble but ignorant man, who has no knowledge of the classics and is interested in mere commercial and administrative matters. On the other hand, he implies, the Irish are scholars and are interested in higher cultural and spiritual matters. He is suggesting here an absolute difference between the materialistic English, whose language is appropriate to market trading, and the spiritual Irish, whose language is associated with the learned languages of the ancient Greek and Roman civilisations. Maire then shows that not all the Irish are interested purely in these spiritual and cultural aspects of life. She simply wants to improve her prospects of doing well materially in the world, and for that she needs to learn the English language.

Irony is used twice in this extract as a technique to undermine what Hugh is telling us. The first example is that Hugh claims that English is particularly suited to the 'purposes of commerce', implying that Gaelic is above commercial and material things, but, ironically, he then shouts to Manus for a slice of soda bread, showing us inadvertently that Gaelic is equally used to gain material needs. The second example is that Hugh proposes that Gaelic has a much closer relationship with the classical languages than English, but the irony is that throughout the extract Hugh is asking pupils to explain the Latin roots of *English* words. The relationship between English and Latin is therefore shown to be as close as the relationship between Gaelic and Latin. Both examples of irony work because the language that we are to believe is spoken is Gaelic, whereas in fact the language spoken is English. What the play shows the audience inadvertently is that Gaelic can be a commercial language and that English has very strong roots in Latin.

LANGUAGE AND STYLE

There are differences in how various characters use language. The clearest example in this extract is between Hugh and Maire. Hugh is highly articulate. If anything, he parades his knowledge of vocabulary before his pupils as if he needed to prove something to them. He uses unusual words such as 'verecund', 'perambulations' and 'conjugation', partly to test his students on their vocabulary, but also to display his own language skills. In contrast, Maire plays down her knowledge of language. She knows exactly what 'perambulations' means, but it is not a word she is ever likely to use. She tends to speak in short sentences which are repetitive: 'That's what my mother says. That's what I say. That's what Dan O'Connell said last month in Ennis'. Likewise, one could not imagine Hugh speaking the above lines. The differences between Hugh and Maire in their language use indicates differences in character and attitude. In some ways, Maire is more confident than Hugh. He seems to need to use a more complex, or highly crafted style in language to show that he is a learned man. Instead of saying 'hello' when he enters the school, for example, he says 'Vesperal salutations to you all'. This may indicate a defensiveness on Hugh's part, a fear that he must prove that he is learned in ways which are immediately, audibly apparent, particularly as his school is soon to be threatened by the new national school.

Staging

Much of the dramatic tension of *Translations* when it is performed on stage is created out of the contrast between cultural identities and attitudes. Lancey and Hugh differ hugely in temperament, attitudes and values, and their differences form part of the play's tension, which develops into a final destructive climax. Hugh and Maire differ greatly in their attitudes to their own culture, and Maire's demand to know English, and Hugh's refusal to teach her, form part of the tension of the play too. These tensions are presented differently on stage in the play. In this extract, we find out what Lancey represents and how he is opposed to Hugh through the device of Hugh telling the class. By doing it this way, Friel has prepared the audience for Lancey before he appears. No argument need take place between Lancey and Hugh to show us the differences between them, because we have already been presented with information about these differences in the scene extracted above. The contrast between Hugh and Maire, on the other hand, is presented through the device of an argument. The stage directions indicate that Hugh treats Maire indifferently, not noticing her gestures, and making her feel uneasy in challenging his authority. But they also indicate that Maire is capable of being determined and sticking to her demand to be taught English. By using these two very different techniques of staging debate, Friel reserves the more serious clash between the Irish and the English until the final Act, and allows the audience to see a clash with less force, between a 'girl' and her 'master'.

How these two contrasts are performed on stage is crucial. Hugh will be seated calmly and assuredly at the front of the class, and Maire will, when addressing herself to him, be resolute but nonetheless will appear to be small and powerless. If Hugh refuses, she has very few tricks up her sleeve to achieve her goal. So, the argument between Maire and Hugh has less dramatic power than the potential clash between Hugh and Lancey. Lancey will look like a powerful figure on his arrival, dressed in uniform and ready to dish out instructions to the natives. Hugh looks equally powerful, as an authority in Baile Beag, and as a large man with a walking stick and an articulate commanding voice. A clash between these two would have immense dramatic power, as it would **symbolise** the clash of Gaelic and English authorities. That is why Friel must find ways in staging the play of holding back that clash until the last Act, when Hugh capitulates, of course, and accepts that his own language and culture will yield to English pressure.

TEXT 2 (from **ACT II SCENE 2 PAGES 51–2**; *from* YOLLAND: Maire. *to* MAIRE: Take me away...)

This scene occurs towards the end of Act II, Scene 2, in which Yolland and Maire have come away from a dance together. At first they are awkward with each other. Maire is embarrassed at being alone with Yolland, and says to him 'Manus'll wonder where I've got to'. They cannot understand each other's language, but their looks and movements will suggest that they are attracted to each other. In this extract Yolland and Maire find a way of communicating their affection for each other through the poetic sound of the place-names. This brings them together, they caress and kiss, but the scene continues with Sarah watching them kissing before running off to tell Manus.

CHARACTERS

In the next Act, when Yolland has gone missing, Maire recalls their romantic evening together, and how he made some mistakes in Gaelic, telling her 'I'll see you yesterday'. In this scene, however, Yolland's pronunciation of Gaelic place-names is perfect, and it is his enthusiasm for Maire, for the language, and for the place which is conveyed to the audience. Yolland has fallen in love with all three, and what we witness in this scene is how much he wants to belong to Baile Beag. He is indeed an enthusiastic hibernophile, as Owen remarks of him in Act I. Yolland wants to live with Maire in Baile Beag and to be able to communicate with her, but the only way he can do that at this stage is to recite place-names. **Ironically**, he knows these place-names so well because he is involved in eradicating them.

Maire is nervous of her feelings for Yolland, and before the extract quoted above she has appeared to be embarrassed and shy. But when he speaks the names of the surrounding villages and townlands of her home, she is moved by them and responds to Yolland. She is clearly in love with him, and wants to run away with him to other places. Maire is desperate to get out of Baile Beag, and part of her dream to escape now involves Yolland. She is tender towards him, and seems to understand his desperation to fit in with the local community. She is depicted here as sensitive and emotional, yet also a daring idealist, who is willing to put at risk her relationship with Manus for a romantic dream, and a man with whom she has fallen in love but about whom she knows very little other than his daily routine.

RECURRENT THEMES AND TECHNIQUES

Translation is the key theme of this scene. When Lancey or Yolland speaks to the Irish characters, for the most part they need Owen to translate for them. This is acceptable for official business, but Yolland wishes to communicate his private feelings to Maire. An interpreter would hardly be appropriate, so Yolland must find a way of communicating to a woman when they do not have a language in common. When he speaks her name she does not respond, but, in the Gaelic place-names of the area around Baile Beag, Yolland finds a language which she can speak too. They move closer together, each speaking but apparently in different languages, until they do seem to be able to understand each other. They speak towards the end of this scene as if they understood every word spoken by each other. But there are also hints of potential disagreements, which the language barrier prevents from becoming apparent. Yolland wants to stay in Baile Beag, whereas Maire is intent on getting out of the village. As Yolland seems to love the place as much as he loves Maire, and as Maire talks throughout the play of leaving Baile Beag, this is bound to cause tension between them. The limited means which they have of communicating with each other prevents this tension from surfacing, however.

The significance of place-names is apparent in this scene, as it is evident in debates and arguments elsewhere in the play. Through the beauty of the Gaelic names, Yolland finds a way of communicating with Maire. It is particularly the exotic sound of those names which must appeal to the English-speaking audience as a kind of poetry. In translation, they are hardly romantic or poetic at all: mouth of the river, black ridge, hole of the sheep, fort of Maol, fort of the foreigner, and so on. Only in the strangeness of the language do the names have any poetic or romantic significance, just as Maire will recite the names of English villages – Little Walsingham, Barton Bendish, Saxingham Nethergate – for the same poetic effect which comes of not knowing their meaning. This would suggest that Friel is writing for an audience which he knows will have scant knowledge of the Gaelic language, and he is possibly mocking Irish audiences by turning the place-names of their own country into exotic poetry.

Language and style

The sound of the Gaelic language gives this scene its poetic tone. Yolland and Maire pick up on the sounds of the names. When Yolland says 'Lis na nGall', Maire follows with 'Lis na nGradh'. By the repetition of 'Lis' and the 'nG' sound, a rhythm is created. They continue by repeating 'carraig', 'loch', 'machaire' and 'cnoc'. The 'poem' of exotic Gaelic names is completed when they rhyme the word 'Mullach' (pronounced Mull-luck) with the last three names 'Port', 'Tor', and 'Lag' (pronounced Lug).

There is also in this scene an interesting difference between Yolland's expressions of love and Maire's. She tends to express her feelings by describing his body – 'soft hands', 'your arms are long and thin', and 'the skin on your shoulders is very white'. But Yolland expresses more subjective feelings – 'I spend my days either thinking of you or gazing up at your house' and 'I would tell you how beautiful you are'. This reverses the way that they have spoken to each other about the wet grass earlier in the scene, when Maire was expressing subjective feelings about the grass and Yolland was describing objectively the condition of the grass.

STAGING

Movement and gesture play a key part in communicating the feelings of Yolland and Maire in this scene, and on stage their movements must be choreographed perfectly to respond to certain words and gestures. They move closer as the poetry of names becomes more intense, until they are face to face and touching each other when they have finished reciting the names. Although Maire's descriptions of Yolland may sound detached and unromantic – e.g. 'your arms are long and thin' – they are holding hands, and the gestures which they make can alter how the audience interprets their words. Gestures also form a common language for Maire and Yolland. When Maire says 'You're trembling', Yolland understands and says 'Yes, I'm trembling because of you'. Presumably, some gesture has been made by Maire which indicates that she refers to his trembling hands. The lighting is also important in conveying the atmosphere of the scene. The stage directions at the beginning advise that the lighting indicate that the scene is outside, and that the barnhouse is concealed by darkness. This would envelop the two in a moonlight effect, perhaps, with darkness surrounding, thereby creating a sense of intimacy between Maire and Yolland and a sense of insularity protecting them from the world outside. That sense of insularity is, of course, broken at the end of the scene when Sarah enters to see them kissing.

TEXT 3   (from **ACT II SCENE I PAGES** 42–3; *from* YOLLAND:
I mean… *to* HUGH: The phrase goes…)

This extract is taken from Act II, Scene 1, in which Yolland and Owen have been engaged in filling in the Name-Book with the new anglicised place-names. Hugh disturbs them when he emerges from upstairs. They begin to talk, and Yolland explains to Hugh his fascination with all things Irish. Hugh is happy to discuss with him the richness of Gaelic language and literature, and to advise Yolland about how to feel less alienated in Baile Beag. Owen gets irritated by his father's 'pompous' talk, and tries to embarrass him. Hugh then leaves them to their work, and Owen and Yolland proceed to have an argument about whether or not to change a Gaelic name to a more anglicised form.

CHARACTERS

Hugh is eloquent in his descriptions of the Gaelic language and literature. He expresses the view that what Irish people lack in material possessions or wealth, they compensate for in spiritual and intellectual riches. Although he refers to Yolland throughout the scene as 'sir' and 'Lieutenant', he seems to be kind and friendly towards the young English soldier who is so interested in everything Irish. He explains in a good-natured manner the roots of Gaelic literature and his own work on language and translation. He even offers Yolland advice about how to become a part of their community more fully, in response to Yolland telling him how isolated he feels from the people of Baile Beag. But is there also a hint of **irony** in Hugh's descriptions of language and literature? When he describes the richness of Gaelic literature as 'our only method of replying to ... inevitabilities', for example, is he not referring to the pressures which English colonialism has put on the language and culture of the Gaelic-speaking people? The pause before the word 'inevitabilities' suggests that he is calculating the effect of a phrase which is critical of English colonialism. Similarly, with the final sentence in this extract, he calculates the effect in the same manner. The pause before 'fact', where 'fact' refers to the certain imposition of the English language on the people, may indicate that Hugh is making thinly veiled criticisms of the English soldier for what his uniform represents. On the surface, then, Hugh seems to be benevolent towards the soldier, but perhaps all his comments are laced with criticisms. After all, telling Yolland that a rich literature compensates for material poverty is a clever way of pointing out to him that the people are indeed desperately poor.

Yolland seems to be unaware in this extract of any irony in Hugh's descriptions of Gaelic language and literature, although he does say later that Hugh 'knows what's happening'. Yolland instead seems to be like a schoolboy, enthralled by the master's eloquent tales of culture and history. He is deferential and humble before Hugh, and shows a keen interest in learning from the school master. He is bearing the signs of the romantic idealist, the sentimental stage-Englishman, who has fallen hopelessly in love with Baile Beag and its people and is innocent of anything suspicious or critical in their dealings with him.

Owen is embarrassed by his father's 'pompous' statements. He tells Hugh to 'stop that nonsense', perhaps because he realises that Hugh is deliberately playing up before Yolland, or indeed that Hugh is mocking Yolland's sentimentality for Gaelic culture. To prevent Hugh from embarrassing, or criticising, Yolland, Owen decides to embarrass his father by reading out the new names of local places, and showing Hugh that, if Yolland feels alienated from this community, so too, Hugh has been alienated from his own landscape. Owen is, then, trying to steer a middle course between Hugh and Yolland here, and to keep Hugh from making Yolland feel any more 'cut off' from the people than he already does. In doing this, Owen is either making heroic efforts to reconcile the two cultures, English and Irish, by protecting Yolland from feeling alienated, or he is betraying his own people in order to please his English friends.

RECURRENT THEMES AND TECHNIQUES
The people of Baile Beag are in a state of transition, from one language and culture to another, and Hugh is reflecting on what such change means. He explains that Gaelic society believes that its cultural traditions and its language are immemorial, that they have endured unaltered for centuries, possibly even millennia. Its place-names seem to reflect the permanence of the natural features of the landscape or traditional elements of Gaelic lifestyles. Faced with this sense of a long tradition and culture which is alien to him, Yolland seems overcome with awe and admiration. But Hugh tells him that he must by all means try to learn the Gaelic language so that he doesn't feel so alienated from the people, but that words are only 'signals, counters. They are not immortal'. Hugh tells Yolland that it might be worth learning Gaelic, but not to worry too much as it looks as though everybody in Baile Beag might be speaking English soon in any case. This sense of transition is important throughout the play, but here Hugh hints that there is something already present in Gaelic culture which may precipitate change anyway: 'it can happen that a civilisation can be imprisoned in a linguistic contour which no longer matches the landscape of ... fact'. Hugh is suggesting here that a culture which has based itself on the strength of its antiquity is not prepared for a giant leap into the modern world, and that is the challenge facing Gaelic society in 1833, and indeed Northern Irish society in 1980.

Irony is evident in Hugh's descriptions of the richness of the vocabulary and literature of Gaelic. The Irish people may spend all their energies on the beauties and complexities of their language, but what Hugh also makes clear is that, if the language which they speak has become redundant, then they have wasted their efforts. Gaelic may possess 'a syntax opulent with tomorrows', but as Hugh then suggests, the language itself might not have any tomorrows.

LANGUAGE AND STYLE

Hugh is calm and confident in the way he expresses himself, whereas Yolland is more excited and defers to Hugh's authority. This difference between them is evident in the manner of their speech. Hugh's speech is articulate and self-assured. He speaks in sentences which are, for the most part, well constructed and premeditated. He pauses, it seems, only for effect, before he says a word which he wants to emphasise. And despite the fact that Owen mocks him for being absent-minded, Hugh is masterful in his control of language. Yolland is less than masterful, however. He changes direction in the middle of a sentence – 'And your Gaelic literature – you're a poet yourself'. He also stammers with excitement – 'It – it – it's really astonishing'. These are the means by which Friel communicates the relationship between the two characters.

Similarly, the differences between Hugh and Owen are illustrated by the ways in which they both speak. Hugh is eloquent and long-winded, almost pompous in his speech. He utters abstract ideas – 'We like to think we endure around truths immemorially posited'. Owen, on the other hand, is direct and simple. He counters his father's eloquence by asking him to 'stop that nonsense'. He speaks in short, uncomplicated sentences, unlike his father.

STAGING

The degree of irony, mockery, bitterness or sarcasm in this scene will depend on how it is performed by each of the actors. Hugh's facial gestures and his tone of voice will alter how the audience interprets the scene. If his intention is to remind Yolland that he is part of the colonial destruction of Gaelic culture, how might he look and sound when he says the word 'inevitabilities'? If he is mocking the ridiculous notion that the Irish enjoy their poverty because they're a spiritual people, perhaps he would sneer or raise his eyebrows when he tells Yolland that 'you could call us a spiritual people'. Does Yolland realise that he is being mocked or criticised by Hugh? How might he make his awareness apparent on stage? He might nod and smile at Hugh at the words 'inevitabilities' and 'fact', indicating that he knows what Hugh is referring to. Yolland might not be so sentimental and naïve as he appears to be, and might indicate by facial gestures that he is capable of understanding the 'subtexts' or implications of what Hugh is saying. These are some of the issues of interpretation which might affect a performance of the play.

PART FIVE

BACKGROUND

BRIAN FRIEL'S LIFE AND WORK

Brian Friel was born in Omagh, County Tyrone in Northern Ireland on 5 January 1929. His father was a teacher from Derry city, and his mother was from a Gaelic-speaking area of County Donegal. When he was ten years old he moved with his family to Derry, where he attended St Columb's College, a Catholic boys school. He then went to the Irish Republic to study for the priesthood in St Patrick's College, Maynooth, but left three years later to begin a teacher's training course in St Joseph's College, Belfast. He worked as a teacher in Derry throughout the 1950s, during which time he began to write short stories. He married, in 1954, Anne Morrison, with whom he would have five children. By 1955 he was publishing stories in American magazines, and three years later he wrote several radio plays which were performed on BBC radio.

In 1960 Friel left the teaching profession and became a full-time writer. His reputation as a playwright grew throughout the 1960s. His first stage play, *The Enemy Within*, was produced at the Abbey Theatre in Dublin. His knowledge and understanding of stage techniques, however, were greatly enhanced by a visit to fellow Ulsterman, Tyrone Guthrie, in Minneapolis, USA, where Guthrie ran a theatre company. Friel continued to publish short stories at the same time as his plays were becoming increasingly renowned.

He moved over the border to the Irish Republic in 1967, to Muff first, and, after 1982, to Greencastle, both in Donegal. He was troubled deeply by the outbreak of sectarian and political conflict in Northern Ireland in 1969, and he responded in his plays to the historical and political issues raised in this conflict. In 1980 Friel teamed up with the actor Stephen Rea to produce Friel's new play, *Translations*, but could only get funding from the Northern Ireland Arts Council for a theatre company rather than a play. They decided, therefore, to found a theatre company which they called 'Field Day'. The Field Day Theatre Company has proved to be one of the most important developments in contemporary Irish theatre. It was based in Derry city and brought world theatrical premieres to this city, before touring in London, New York and the provincial towns of Ireland. It attempted to draw on the Catholic and Protestant traditions of Northern Ireland in an effort to bring the two communities closer together.

Friel wrote some of his most innovative plays, *Translations* and *Making History* , in the 1980s, and had them produced by Field Day. He later resigned from Field Day, in 1994, on the grounds that he believed artistic integrity was being compromised by the political arguments which were surrounding the company. He has been acknowledged for his tremendous achievements in drama and literature, however. The Republic of Ireland appointed him as a senator in the Irish Senate, the upper house of government, in 1987. In 1989 he was honoured by the BBC for his achievements in modern drama when they put on a six-play season of his plays, the first time the BBC has honoured a living playwright in this way.

H IS WRITINGS

Friel's writing career can be divided roughly into three phases. In the first phase, from 1952 to 1964, he wrote short stories, radio plays and stage plays which were chiefly preoccupied with the private individual, and with the effects of childhood experiences on adult life, but there are also hints of later concerns with communication difficulties and with Irishness. His publishing career began in 1955 when he published two stories in *The New Yorker*. He then had two radio plays performed on BBC Northern Ireland Radio and BBC Radio – *A Sort of Freedom* and *To This Hard House*. His first stage play to be produced was *The Enemy Within*, a play about St Columba's dilemma in Iona between his religious calling and the demands of his family and home in Ireland. It was performed first at the Abbey Theatre in Dublin in 1962.

In the second phase of his career, from 1964 to 1988, Friel concentrated mostly on plays, which showed a growing interest in exploring the impact of national and global historical forces on the lives of private individuals and local communities, reaching what are generally regarded to be his greatest achievements in *Translations* in 1980 and *Making History* in 1988. During this period he was exploring controversial subjects – Irish emigration (*Philadelphia, Here I Come,*

1964), the political independence of the Republic of Ireland (*The Mundy Scheme*, 1969), the shooting of innocent civilians in Derry city (*The Freedom of the City*, 1973), the destruction of Gaelic language and culture (*Translations*, 1980) and the clash of Irish and English military forces in the late sixteenth century (*Making History*, 1988).

After 1988, in the third phase of his career, he turned away from writing plays as national **epics** or **historical dramas,** and seemed to concentrate on earlier personal and autobiographical themes. *Dancing at Lughnasa* (1990), *Molly Sweeney* (1994) and *Give Me Your Answer, Do!* (1997) all address concerns with the individual psyche and personal liberation more closely than was evident throughout the 1960s, seventies and eighties. There are two ways of seeing this return in his later career to personal themes. The first is that he is retreating from the controversial historical and political issues for which he became famous and was heavily criticised. The second is that he felt that he had written everything he wanted to say about larger historical and political themes after he finished *Making History* in 1988, and has since moved on.

HISTORICAL AND LITERARY BACKGROUND

HISTORICAL BACKGROUND

In 1833, the year in which *Translations* is set, Ireland remained a predominantly rural, Catholic, Gaelic-speaking country. It was under English colonial rule, as a result of a series of invasions and plantations which took place between 1169 and 1603, and had been annexed to Britain in the 1801 Act of Union. Under colonial rule, the Irish people suffered a number of disadvantages. They were punished for belonging to Catholic or Dissenter religions when England was an Anglican-Protestant country. They were forbidden to practise non-Anglican faiths or to receive an education. They were also barred from owning land of any substantial amount and from entering professional occupations. These 'penal laws' were enforced throughout the country until the end of the eighteenth century, and they were not removed fully until 1829 with the Catholic Emancipation Act. By that time, the laws had caused considerable damage to Irish society and culture. Catholics were allowed to become traders and merchants, for example, but to do so they invariably had to learn the English language. So too, Catholics could become landowners if they converted to the Anglican faith. There was always a cost involved for an individual to advance up the social and economic ladder. By the beginning of the nineteenth century, this had created a situation in which the middle and upper classes in Ireland spoke English, were predominantly Anglican-Protestant, and either owned land or worked in professional occupations in the towns, while the lower classes in Ireland spoke Gaelic, were predominantly Catholic, and were tenants on the land with small holdings and no legal protection from unfair rents or eviction.

This division in Irish society resulted in disaffection and resentment among the lower classes. Many chose to emigrate to the United States, where they believed they could start a new better life, without fear of discrimination or poverty. Others chose to rebel against British rule, by taking up arms against the colonial army. The play reflects these responses in a number of ways: Maire chooses to emigrate; Hugh and Jimmy Jack were inspired to take up arms against Britain in the 1798 Rebellion, although they didn't get very far; and the Donnelly twins are believed to be organising their own campaigns of local violent resistance against the English soldiers in Baile Beag. Irish Catholics and Dissenters had also found ways of evading the penal laws. Local communities gathered together to practise their faiths in open-air rock masses or barn services in remote places, where the authorities would not find them, and they had also formed hedge-schools, so called because they were at first held in hedgerows. Later they moved into more stable lodgings, such as the cow-shed Hugh uses in the play.

In the early nineteenth century, the population of Ireland grew rapidly, to a peak of over 8 million people in 1841. The land was divided and subdivided between the sons of farmers who already lived on smallholdings, until many of the farms, particularly in the west of Ireland, were unable to sustain even the most meagre existence. The Irish people turned to the potato crop as the staple ingredient in their diet. It would grow in abundance, with little attention, and it contained most of the nourishment they needed. They became dependent on the potato crop, but it was struck by blight and disease fourteen times between 1816 and 1842, including the year 1833. A fungus attacked the potato plant in damp and muggy conditions, the leaves withered and turned black, and the potatoes decomposed and emitted a sweet stench of decay. This is what Bridget smells several times in the play. Potato crops were devastated, and the failure of the British government to provide adequate relief measures, which caused the Great Famine of 1845 to 1850, during which 1 million people died and 1.5 million emigrated to Britain and America. The majority of the people who died or emigrated came from the west and south of the country, from the poor, Gaelic-speaking communities like Baile Beag. This is the significance of Bridget's fear of the smell of rotting potatoes. Friel is reminding his audience that disaster awaits this community in the future.

Hedge-schools

Hedge-schools were set up on an informal and makeshift basis in local communities throughout Ireland in response to the penal laws enacted by England preventing Irish Catholics and Dissenters from receiving an education. At first, they took place in hedgerows, with one pupil assigned to keep watch for English soldiers. The school master was paid small fees, sometimes by way of provisions and crops (or milk in Maire's case), for tuition in arithmetic, reading and writing. In the eighteenth century, when the enforcement of the penal laws was relaxed in most areas, the hedge-schools moved into more permanent homes, such as barns or stables. In most of the hedge-schools instruction was given through the medium of the Irish language, and in many, Latin, Greek, Mathematics and other subjects were taught too, particularly in the southwest of Ireland. There are a number of accounts of English travellers coming across classical scholars such as Hugh and Jimmy Jack in the midst of remote rural societies. School masters were well versed in most subjects, such as history, geography, the classical languages and literatures, mathematics, and the Irish and English languages. Some even knew and taught navigation, astronomy and surveying. Some were renowned Gaelic poets, whose teaching gave them a steady income and allowed them the leisure to write. The hedge-schools were also well served by textbooks and instruction manuals. Hugh's planned volume on languages, 'The Pentaglot Preceptor', was in fact a book published by a school master in Dublin, Patrick Lynch, in 1796.

The hedge-schools were a form of rebellion against English colonial rule, and would certainly have been greeted with suspicion by English soldiers or civil servants. Most of the legitimate schools in Ireland had been created for the purposes of spreading the English language or the Anglican faith, so that the hedge-schools represented a threat to the establishment of an English, Protestant culture in Ireland. The hedge-schools were organised on a local basis only, but they spread rapidly across the country, and came from the desire among the peasants themselves for instruction. As Ireland became more anglicised in the later eighteenth century, the peasants increasingly felt the need to communicate in English, particularly for the purposes of trading at fairs and markets, and they put pressure on the hedge-school masters to instruct them and their children through the medium of English. This became the main language of most of the hedge-schools in the early nineteenth century. By the 1820s, the hedge-schools had become so widespread that the British government felt compelled to introduce a state system of education. Chief Secretary Stanley did so in 1831, creating what became known as the national schools, which instructed children through the medium of the English language solely and which charged no fees. This new system of national education made the hedge-schools redundant, and had a devastating effect on the use of the Gaelic language and indeed on the tradition of classical and historical learning in Ireland. However, even though the hedge-schools were a vital source of education and training in Ireland in the eighteenth and early nineteenth centuries, they did not benefit everyone. In Donegal, the setting of the play, some 62 per cent of the population were still illiterate in 1841.

ORDNANCE SURVEY

As a result of the British army's need for more accurate maps of Ireland, and as a result of growing dissatisfaction among taxpayers and government officials with existing, inadequate surveys of land sizes and values in Ireland, the British government consented to organise the first complete ordnance survey map of Ireland, at a scale of six inches to a mile. It was proclaimed that the map should be taken as 'proof of the disposition of the [British] legislature to adopt all measures calculated to advance the interests of Ireland' (Andrews, 1975, p. 308), as it showed that Britain was bringing the benefits of greater scientific knowledge of map-making and mathematics to Ireland. Many maps of Ireland had been made by previous generations of English settlers and soldiers, some for the purposes of marking out land which had been confiscated from the Irish, others for the purposes of providing the army with more accurate information about troubled areas. But none had been as complete or as accurate as the ordnance survey conducted between 1824 and 1846 under the direction of Colonel Thomas Colby of the Royal Engineers.

From the very beginning, the possibility of the survey being undertaken by Irish engineers and agents was dismissed, and the job was passed over to the ordnance survey unit of the Royal Engineers. Work began in the area in which the play is set, in the northwest of Ireland, in 1827 and was completed in 1840. Some of the maps from this area were published in 1833, however. In addition to producing a more accurate map, the engineers were also given the task of standardising the place-names. They kept 'name-books' in which they recorded new names which they believed simplified and anglicised the spelling and pronunciation of the old Gaelic names. The government also employed an Irish scholar, John O'Donovan, to translate Gaelic names, and to standardise Gaelic spelling, much like Owen O'Donnell in the play. The 'name-books' took longer to complete than the maps, largely because the survey teams were often divided about what names to give to townlands, particularly whether they should try to capture the meaning of Gaelic names (e.g. Bun na hAbhann, meaning foot of the river, might become 'riverfoot') or try to replicate the sound of the names in English spelling (e.g. Bun na hAbhann, pronounced Bun-na-how-en, might be simplified to Bunowen). Friel's play is largely accurate in its depiction of the work of the surveyors. Some of them, like Yolland in the play, did become interested in the history of the places which they were mapping, and were sensitive to what the local residents felt about name changes or about details of the map. Friel even borrows the names of the officers, Lancey and Yolland, from real officers who worked on the ordnance survey teams. Where real life differs from the play is that the engineers did not carry arms and were never called upon to conduct evictions, searches or any form of physical violence against the local populations. Friel seems to be conflating deliberately the destruction of Irish place-names by the engineers with the destruction of Irish people's houses, farms and livelihoods by colonising soldiers.

NORTHERN IRELAND IN 1980

Translations was first produced in Derry in 1980, eleven years after the sectarian and political conflict in Northern Ireland began. Ireland had been partitioned into six northern counties and twenty-six southern counties in 1920, creating two separate states. The south became independent from Britain in 1922 while the north remained a colony of Britain with its own parliament. The six counties of Northern Ireland had been chosen because they contained a majority of Protestant people, who feared that they would be attacked and marginalised in independent, mostly Catholic, Ireland. As a result of partition, Protestants outnumbered Catholics in Northern Ireland by a ratio of 9:7, and electoral boundaries were established so as to ensure that the Unionist party, which most Protestant people supported, would always win. This party held power in Northern Ireland from 1920 to 1972, during which time it failed to do anything to stop the routine discrimination against Catholics in employment, housing, local government representation and in other basic civil rights, and failed to stop a sectarian police force from attacking and discriminating against Catholics. The Catholic people organised civil rights protests in the late 1960s, but were assaulted and beaten by loyalist gangs and paramilitary police units.

In response to the outrageous behaviour of the police, some Catholic areas of Derry and Belfast erected barricades and refused to allow police units to enter, but these areas were stormed by loyalist and police gangs. Violent clashes began to erupt across the province in 1969, and the British army was called in by the Unionist government to preserve the peace. A small minority of nationalists in Catholic areas, calling themselves the Provisional Irish Republican Army (IRA) saw this as the opportunity to use violence to overthrow the state, and began a campaign of guerrilla war against the army and police. Loyalist gangs responded to their attacks with more violence, and the war in Northern Ireland began. By 1980 many thousands of civilians, policemen, soldiers and gunmen had been killed and injured. In 1979 alone, the IRA had assassinated the Northern Ireland spokesman for the Conservative party, the British ambassador to the Netherlands and Earl Mountbatten, the former viceroy of India, and had killed eighteen soldiers of the Parachute Regiment in a bomb attack in south county Down. In addition to the campaign of violence, IRA prisoners began to go on hunger strike to protest against the government's treatment of them as criminals rather than political prisoners. By the time *Translations* was produced, in September 1980, ten prisoners had starved themselves to death, and riots had erupted across Northern Ireland after every death. It was one of the worst years of violence and suffering in the history of the war.

Friel's play does not reflect directly on this context, but, in representing a struggle between the rebellious Donnelly twins and a ruthless army in Act III, it does suggest a parallel with the conflict in Northern Ireland between the IRA and the British army. The characters of the play also represent a broad spectrum of political views. Lancey is the determined and stiff officer, who is capable of ruthlessness when he feels that it is necessary. The Donnelly twins, although we never meet them, are obviously the hardened rebels, resolute in opposing the army with hit-and-run raids. In between those two extremes, Yolland is the soldier who is liberal and sentimental about Ireland, Maire is the Irish girl who is sentimental about England, Doalty and Manus are sympathetic to the Donnelly twins but only take up violent or rebellious measures when they are pushed into it, and Hugh clings to his Gaelic traditions until he realises that they are becoming outdated. Each of these characters represents a potential response to the conflict in Northern Ireland – to toughen security measures, to take up arms against the state, or to compromise and make peace. Friel seems to favour those characters who are compromisers – Yolland, Maire and Hugh – who learn to love those from other cultures and to embrace other cultures for the possibilities they offer, rather than to spurn them out of fear. These characters have the capacity to put fear and the past behind them, and they have much to offer in the context of Northern Irish politics as role models of reconciliation.

CONTEMPORARY LANGUAGE DEBATES

Ireland is largely an English-speaking country today, despite the fact that the constitution of the Republic of Ireland claims that Gaelic is the first language of the nation. It has been the aspiration of the Irish government, for much of the twentieth century, to revive the use of the Gaelic language. Gaelic is a compulsory part of primary and secondary education, for example, and successive governments have funded a Gaelic language radio station, television programmes, and cultural organisations to promote fluency in the language. But Gaelic is still a minority language in Ireland, as was evident in a government survey of attitudes to the language in 1975. Only 2.7 per cent of Irish people were found to have 'native speaker' ability, and a further 10.8 per cent could understand 'most conversations'. In contrast, some 80 per cent of Irish people were shown to be consistently indifferent to the Gaelic language. These statistics proved that, even when Ireland was independent from Britain, and its people were free to speak or learn whichever language they chose, the majority of them did not know or use the Gaelic language.

Translations was written in the aftermath of the government survey, at a time when there was intense debate about the future of the Gaelic language. As Declan Kiberd has argued, 'the play is an uncompromising reminder that it is Irish, and not English people, who have the power to decide which language is spoken in Ireland' (Kiberd, 1995, p. 616). The play asks audiences to believe that much of the dialogue is in the Gaelic language, but this is an indictment of the lack of knowledge of the language among Irish audiences. If the play is about the tragedy of a language which has been devastated and made almost redundant, Friel is also highlighting the **irony** of having to tell the story of this tragedy in the language which replaced Gaelic. The Irish audiences might laugh at the inability of Yolland and Lancey to communicate in Gaelic to the villagers, but the play is also showing those audiences that they are in the same position as the English soldiers, needing to have Gaelic, as well as Greek and Latin, translated into English for them.

LITERARY BACKGROUND

Brian Friel was one of a number of writers in Northern Ireland who sought to explain the violence and conflict of the 1970s. The divisions and tensions in Northern Ireland since 1969 forced writers such as Friel, Seamus Heaney, Tom Paulin and John Montague to examine their own cultural histories and identities for the causes and the possible solutions to 'the troubles'. Heaney, for example, through poems such as 'The Tollund Man' and 'The Bog Queen', explored images of ancient murder victims discovered in bogs as a means of describing and understanding the horror of violence and killing in contemporary Northern Ireland. Heaney suggested that poetry could be a kind of excavation of cultural identity, with the poet digging through the soil of history to uncover the roots of modern disturbances. Friel might be seen as using the form of drama to explore the relevance for contemporary Ireland of the myths and conflicts of the past, and he does this in a number of his plays, most notably *Translations*, *Making History* and *Volunteers*.

As language and names are contentious issues in Northern Ireland, with the very name of the province and some of its towns the subject of fierce argument, it is not surprising to find Northern Irish writers fascinated with the history of linguistic traditions and changes in place-names. John Montague published a poem in 1972 called 'A Lost Tradition' which mourned the loss of Gaelic place-names. He wrote: 'The whole landscape a manuscript / We had lost the skill to read / A part of our past disinherited'. It is this feeling of disinheritance from their own cultural traditions which writers such as Montague, Heaney and Friel have explored as a way of articulating the problems with cultural identity for the people of Northern Ireland. The Catholic people of the province felt that they had been dispossessed of the Gaelic language, while among the Protestant people there were sizeable numbers who had once spoken Ulster-Scots. Tom Paulin proposed a compromise solution to the language question by advocating the use of Hiberno-English as a literary language.

THE FIELD DAY THEATRE COMPANY

Most of these writers were involved in the Field Day Theatre Company, which was founded in 1980 by Brian Friel and Stephen Rea. The reasons for setting up a theatre company were initially expedient, in order to qualify for funding the production of Friel's *Translations* in Derry city. But the company became a lively stimulant of debates and artistic experiments in Ireland. In the programme notes for the first production of *Translations* Friel and Rea gave the following definition of the term 'Field Day' to convey the variety of senses in which they felt the name was appropriate:

Field-day:
A day on which troops are drawn up for exercise in field evolution; a military review; a day occupied with brilliant or exciting events; a day spent in the field, e.g. by the hunt, or by field naturalists.

'Field day' could be about rehearsing strategies, celebrating strength, having fun or exploring nature. As a theatre company and a literary and cultural movement it did all these things. It experimented with cultural identities and histories within the context of Northern Irish politics. Its board of directors consisted of three Protestants and three Catholics, and it did try on several occasions to produce plays and pamphlets which reflected the diverse traditions of Northern Ireland, not just one side of the story. They produced innovative new plays and translations of foreign plays regularly throughout the 1980s and 1990s. They initiated a series of pamphlets on key themes in the cultural debates in Ireland in 1983, which included essays on Anglo-Irish identities, the language debates, cultural stereotypes, nationalism, unionism and colonialism. More recently, they produced a three-volume anthology of Irish writing, from ancient to modern times, and launched a series of academic books on Irish history, culture and literature.

An important dimension of the Field Day projects was that it was based in Derry. The city was an unusual choice, as it was in the northwest corner of Ireland and had traditionally not been regarded as a cultural centre. But it was a city divided in its very name, called Derry by Catholic or nationalist people, and Londonderry by Protestant or unionist people. It was also a frontier city, and had been built in the seventeenth century as a fort to protect English settlers from Irish attacks. It is still a frontier city now, as it lies on the border between the North and the Republic of Ireland. It seemed to be an appropriate city for a theatre company which was interested in healing divisions to begin. Almost every Field Day play premiered in Derry first, before embarking on a tour of London, New York and on tours of provincial towns in Ireland. The directors of Field Day wanted to move away from the idea of drama that could only be seen in the big cities. The theatre company became controversial for its productions, not least because Friel's own plays generated storms of debate about history and cultural identities. It seems to have been partly as a result of these controversies that Friel resigned from the company in 1994.

IRISH DRAMA

Irish drama of the twentieth century has been persistently concerned with a number of key themes and techniques, and Friel's *Translations* follows in the same tradition:

THE RURAL WEST AS A HAVEN OF GAELIC LANGUAGE AND CUSTOMS
This tradition began with W.B. Yeats, Lady Gregory and John M. Synge at the Abbey Theatre in the early years of the twentieth century. Synge in particular presented the west of Ireland as the source of a poor but exotic lifestyle which was alternative in language, morality, social customs and cultural habits to the anglicised east. Friel's play is set in a rural community in the northwest of Ireland, and it does seem to represent the last vestiges of a dying Gaelic community.

THE MOTIVATIONS AND ASPIRATIONS OF IRISH NATIONALISM
Yeats is clearly interested in what makes people take up arms for a nationalist cause, in his play *Cathleen Ni Houlihan*, for example. Sean O'Casey also explored this theme in his Dublin trilogy of plays. Friel investigates the motivation for nationalist action by showing us the gradual turn of men like Manus, Owen and Doalty away from being friendly to English soldiers to being willing to fight against them.

THE TRAGEDY OF KEY MOMENTS IN IRISH HISTORY
Yeats, O'Casey, and Frank McGuinness are good examples of dramatists who have turned back to the past to reflect on the significance of those events for the present, and who have explored the sentiments and perceptions surrounding key historical events. The events of early nineteenth-century Irish history, including the decline of the Gaelic language, the approach of famine, the imposition of tough colonial rule and the rise in the number of Irish people emigrating, are all reflected in *Translations*.

MATERIALIST ENGLAND AND SPIRITUALIST IRELAND

A strong theme in Yeats's plays is the difference between mystical, artistic Ireland and England, which he spurned as shallow and materialistic. In Friel's play Hugh voices this same view.

THE USE OF COMEDY TO UNDERMINE AUTHORITY FIGURES

Sean O'Casey makes fun out of nationalist heroes, in particular, showing us that men who brag about their exploits in warfare are hollow and pathetic. Brendan Behan took this several steps further by making fun of every form of authority – policemen, soldiers, nationalists, civil servants, government officials, priests, prison warders, the upper class, and so on. Friel uses comedy to undermine Hugh, the school master, and Lancey and Yolland, the two officers.

LANGUAGE AS A MEDIUM OF CULTURAL AND POLITICAL IDENTITY

The invention of a peculiar language which indicated a difference between Irish and English cultural identities was the achievement of the earliest Anglo-Irish drama of the seventeenth and eighteenth centuries, with dramatists such as George Farquhar, Thomas Sheridan and Charles Macklin inventing a special inflection of English which indicated to audiences that the characters were Irish. Yeats and Synge partly continued this tradition by inflecting the English of their characters towards Hiberno-English. These dramatists were also accused of making fun of Irish speech, however, and of falsifying Irish ways of speaking. Friel sidesteps this problem by having his characters speaking in English, with hardly a trace of dialect except in the odd colloquial phrase, but having his audience believe that some of them are speaking in Gaelic.

THE ROLE OF VIOLENCE IN IRISH SOCIETY AND HISTORY

Almost all Irish dramatists in the twentieth century have been preoccupied with incidents of violence in Irish society and history, perhaps because this century has seen two lengthy guerrilla wars, the last of which, in Northern Ireland beginning in 1969, has led many writers to assess the place of violence in Ireland. Yeats, Synge, Gregory, O'Casey, Behan, and John B. Keane, to name just a few, have explored the theme of violence. Friel is obviously concerned with the force of colonial violence in *Translations*.

PART SIX

CRITICAL HISTORY & BROADER PERSPECTIVES

REVIEWS AND CONTROVERSIES

The first performance of Friel's *Translations* took place on 23 September 1980 in the Guildhall, Derry. It was directed by Art O'Briain and was presented by the Field Day Theatre Company. It was an instant success, with the opening productions sold out, and it has been almost in constant production in Ireland and elsewhere ever since. It was interpreted first as an attempt to represent early nineteenth-century Ireland accurately on stage, despite the fact that Friel did not intend it to be seen principally as an historical play.

The reviews were generally favourable, but they indicated considerable differences in how the play was interpreted. Colm Cronin of *The Sunday Tribune*, for example, saw the play as a treatise 'on the failure of a people to cherish and preserve the riches of their culture', whereas Fintan O'Toole in *Ireland and the Arts* interpreted the play as being about 'the historical disjunction caused by the forced shift of Irish speech from the Gaelic language to English'. Cronin thought the play was blaming the Irish for losing their language, while O'Toole saw it as blaming the English for destroying Gaelic.

Some critics believed that the play was sanctioning violence, and others believed that it was condemning violence. Martha McClelland, writing for *An Phoblacht*, the newspaper of the IRA, argued that the play was celebrating as heroic Doalty's decision to organise violent resistance to the army: 'It is Doalty who knows how to deal with the present and defend culture most effectively.' Martin Esslin, on the other hand, writing in *Plays and Players*, suggested that the play was highlighting 'the moral dilemma of those in Ireland who desire independence and national freedom but abhor violence in any form'. For Esslin, the play was not celebrating violence, but depicting as tragic the situation in which people felt compelled to fight.

There were also a number of controversies concerning the historical accuracy of the play. The Irish historian Sean Connolly described the play as 'a distortion of the real nature and causes of cultural change in nineteenth-century Ireland so extreme as to go beyond mere factual error'. Particularly controversial were the final scenes in which characters reported seeing the engineers destroying fences, trampling crops and rifling through the countryside with bayonets. J.H. Andrews, who otherwise thought the play was a subtle blend of historical truths, argued in an essay in *The Irish Review* that Friel had represented the engineers inaccurately. The engineers were not permitted to carry out evictions or threats of any kind, and were not armed when they conducted the ordnance survey. Most of the staff of the ordnance survey project were not even English soldiers but Irish civilians. And most of the place-names were not invented by the engineers but had already been anglicised for years, and sometimes centuries, before. Friel's play was criticised for distorting the past and inventing a purely fictitious nationalist version of history. He in turn refuted the suggestion that the play was supposed to be historically accurate at all, and in the programme to *Making History* in 1988 he stated clearly from the outset that 'when there was a tension between historical "fact" and the imperative of fiction, I'm glad to say I kept faith with the narrative'. It is possible to read *Making History*, which features an historian who distorts the facts deliberately for the purpose of inventing a national hero, as a response to the critics who argued that *Translations* was a distortion of history, just as *The Communication Cord* can be read as a response to those critics who argued that *Translations* presented a naïve rural idyll.

Despite these controversies, Friel's *Translations* has become a national classic of Irish drama, and has become renowned worldwide, according to Fintan O'Toole, 'as a definitive statement about the nature and meaning of colonialism'. Friel may have distorted the historical facts, but he has created a masterful piece of dramatic writing which is capable in performance of making the tragedy of the conflict between Ireland and England moving and poignant. O'Toole argued in *The Irish Times* in 1996, on the occasion of the play being revived at the Abbey Theatre, that the play was 'all too accurate about the present', and that it contained an 'underlying feeling for the tragedy of people who get caught up in myths and mindsets that cannot adapt to change'. At a time when the possibilities for peace in Northern Ireland were looking gloomy as a ceasefire was wrecked by people whose mindsets were slow to change, O'Toole argued that the greatest achievement of the play was not its

REVIEWS AND CONTROVERSIES continued

representation of nineteenth-century Ireland but its message to late twentieth-century Ireland that ambiguous and confused identities were worth the price if peace was the result.

FURTHER READING

OTHER WORKS BY BRIAN FRIEL

Selected Plays, Faber and Faber, 1984

Making History, Faber and Faber, 1989

CRITICAL STUDIES OF FRIEL'S PLAYS

Richard Pine, *Brian Friel and Ireland's Drama*, Routledge, 1990
> Pine's book surveys Friel's writings since the 1950s, examining each play and short-story collection in detail. He argues that Friel's *Philadelphia, Here I Come!* marks the beginning of contemporary Irish drama

The following studies of Friel may also be useful:

Ulf Dantanus, *Brian Friel: A Study*, Faber and Faber, 1988

George O'Brien, *Brian Friel*, Gill and Macmillan, 1989

Alan Peacock, ed., *The Achievement of Brian Friel*, Colin Smythe, 1993

FRIEL'S SOURCES FOR

J. H. Andrews, *A Paper Landscape: The Ordnance Survey of Nineteenth-Century Ireland*, Oxford University Press, 1975
> An impressive and comprehensive study of the ordnance survey campaigns in Ireland from 1824 to 1846, Andrews covers the contexts, organisation, methods and results of the campaigns in detail. Friel was fascinated with the ideals and problems of representing the landscape in such detail on a map

P.J. Dowling, *The Hedge Schools of Ireland*, Mercier Press, 1968
> Dowling's short history of the hedge-schools covers the emergence of the schools as a response to the penal laws, how the schools worked and what subjects were

taught there, the nature of the school masters, and the decline of the hedge-school in the early nineteenth century. Many of the details of Friel's school in *Translations* are evidently borrowed from this book

George Steiner, *After Babel: Aspects of Language and Translation*, Oxford University Press, 1975

An influential study of the idea of languages and translation, Steiner's book argues that translation is an activity which we conduct almost every minute of the day and that translation can never be perfect or adequate. Steiner explains theories of language and translation lucidly and simply, and refers to an impressive range of languages and cultures. Friel read and was greatly inspired by this book

Edmund Curtis, *A History of Ireland*, Methuen, 1936

Curtis's history covers a vast sweep of Irish history and has been one of the standard accounts of Irish history since it was first published. Friel quotes from Curtis's book in the programme notes to *Translations*

IRISH DRAMA

Michael Etherton, *Contemporary Irish Dramatists*, Macmillan, 1989

Etherton traces the history of Irish drama from the 1960s to the 1980s, and devotes a lengthy chapter, almost a quarter of the book, to the plays of Brian Friel. Etherton argues that Friel has been instrumental in some of the most exciting developments in contemporary Irish drama

Christopher Murray, *Twentieth Century Irish Drama: Mirror up to Nation*, Manchester University Press, 1997

Murray argues that Irish drama has reflected and shaped the tremendous changes in Irish politics and society in the twentieth century. He examines Friel's role in this process in a chapter on how contemporary dramatists have reflected on the violence and politics of Northern Ireland since 1969

Anthony Roche, Contemporary Irish Drama: From Beckett to McGuinness, Gill and Macmillan, 1994

This book examines the popularity and success of Irish drama since the work of Brendan Behan and Samuel Beckett in the 1950s. It includes chapters on Brian Friel, Thomas Kilroy, Tom Murphy and Northern Irish drama, and celebrates in particular the work of Frank McGuinness

Marilynn J. Richtarik, *Acting Between the Lines: The Field Day Theatre Company and Irish Cultural Politics 1980–1984*, Clarendon Press, Oxford, 1994

> This is a detailed study of the Field Day Theatre Company including the history of its formation and the projects with which it was involved in the first four years of its existence. It includes a chapter on *Translations* which examines the controversies surrounding the historical inaccuracies of the play and the criticisms made in the early reviews

LITERARY AND HISTORICAL BACKGROUND

Reg Hindley, *The Death of the Irish Language*, Routledge, 1990

> Hindley's book traces the decline of the Gaelic language from the eighteenth to the twentieth century, and examines the causes of this decline. It also analyses regional differences in how the language has survived, and explores the various strategies employed in attempting to keep the language alive

J.H. Andrews, *Shapes of Ireland: Maps and their Makers 1564–1839*, Geography Publications, 1997

> A study of the chequered history of English map-making in Ireland, Andrews's book explores in depth the methods, motives and means by which maps were made of Ireland from the sixteenth to the nineteenth century. It includes a chapter on the ordnance survey maps of the early nineteenth century

Declan Kiberd, *Inventing Ireland: The Literature of the Modern Nation*, Jonathan Cape, 1995

> Kiberd's book contains illuminating chapters on Northern Irish writers, and the literary and political contexts in which Friel was writing, as well as an excellent interpretation of Friel's *Translations*. It constructs a careful reading of the play as an exploration of the impact of colonialism and of the various attempts at resistance

A. Norman Jeffares, *Anglo-Irish Literature*, Macmillan, 1982

> Jeffares's study of Irish writing in English is comprehensive and detailed, and analyses the emergence of this tradition of literature from the medieval to the modern period. He barely mentions Friel, but it is a useful guide to the history of Anglo-Irish literature

Robert Welch, ed., *The Oxford Companion to Irish Literature*, Oxford
University Press, 1996

> This book contains entries on key Irish writers, writings, terms and concepts, and
> may be useful when considering Friel in relation to the Irish literary tradition. It
> includes commentaries on Friel and his works, as well as entries on many of Friel's
> plays

S.J. Connolly, ed., *The Oxford Companion to Irish History*, Oxford
University Press, 1998

> This book contains entries on key historical events, figures and trends in Ireland,
> and may be useful in contextualising some elements of Friel's *Translations*. It
> includes entries on hedge-schools, national schools, the ordnance survey and on
> Gaelic Ireland

Events in Ireland	Author's life	Literary events

1603 Enforcement of English law throughout Ireland

1641 Great Catholic-Gaelic Rebellion

1649 Cromwell arrives in Ireland

1650 Catholic landowners exiled

1690 William of Orange defeats James II at Battle of the Boyne

1690-1780 Golden Age of Gaelic Aisling poetry

1695 First penal laws enacted against Catholics

1775 Birth of Daniel O'Connell, campaigner for Catholic emancipation

1780 Brian Merriman, *The Midnight Court*

1800 Ireland annexed to Britain in Act of Union

1800 Maria Edgeworth, *Castle Rackrent*

1816-42 16 crop failures due to potato blight

1823 O'Connell's Catholic Association founded

1824-46 Ordnance survey of Ireland

1829 Catholic Emancipation Act passed (Catholics can now sit as MPs)

1829 Gerald Griffin, *The Collegians*

1831 Creation of National Schools

1833 First Ordnance Survey maps of Ireland published

1841 Irish population reaches 8 million

1845-9 The Great Famine: 1 million die; 1.5 million emigrate

1847 Ireland left to 'operation of natural causes'; Death of O'Connell

1847 William Carleton, *The Black Prophet*

1852 Birth of Lady Augusta Gregory, leading figure in Irish Revival

1856 Birth of George Bernard Shaw

Events in Ireland	Author's life	Literary events
1858 Irish Republican Brotherhood founded; Fenian Brotherhood founded in America		
		1863 Ferguson, *Lays of Western Gael*
		1865 Birth of W.B. Yeats
1867 Fenian rising in Ireland		
		1871 Birth of J.M. Synge
1879 Threat of famine and evictions in Ireland		
		1880 Birth of Sean O'Casey
		1882 Birth of James Joyce
1886 First Home Rule Bill		
1891 Death of Charles Stewart Parnell		
1893 Second Home Rule Bill; foundation of Gaelic League		**1893** D. Hyde, *Love Songs of Connacht*
		1899 Irish Literary Theatre founded
		1900 Birth of Sean O'Faolain, Irish novelist and short story writer
		1902 W.B. Yeats, *Cathleen Ni Houlihan*
		1903 Birth of Frank O'Connor, Irish short story writer
		1904 G.B. Shaw, *John Bull's Other Island*
		1907 J.M. Synge, *Playboy of the Western World*
1912 Third Home Rule Bill: Ulster Volunteer Force founded; Irish Citizens Army and Irish National Volunteers founded		
1914-18 First World War		**1914** George Moore, *Hail and Farewell*
1916 Easter rising, Dublin		
1919 Anglo-Irish Treaty		

Events in Ireland	Author's life	Literary events
1922-3 Civil War; deaths of Michael Collins, Erskine Childers, O'Connor		
		1923 Birth of Brendan Behan
	1929 Birth of **Brian Friel**, Omagh, N. Ireland	
		1932 Death of Lady Gregory
1937 Constitution of 'Eire' - southern Ireland becomes independent of Britain		
1939 IRA bombing campaign in Britain	**1939** Friel family move to Derry	**1939** Death of W.B. Yeats; birth of Seamus Heaney
1939-45 Second World War		
		1941 Death of James Joyce
		1942 Patrick Kavanagh, *The Great Hunger*
1949 Republic of Ireland declared	**1949** Friel graduates from St Patrick's College, Maynooth; starts teacher training at St Joseph's, Belfast, marries Anne Morrison	
	1950 Teaches in Derry	**1950** Death of G.B. Shaw
	1952 Begins writing short stories	
1956-62 IRA campaign in North		
	1958 First radio plays for BBC: *A Sort of Freedom; To This Hard House*	**1958** Brendan Behan's *The Hostage*
	1960 Leaves teaching to write full time	
	1962 First stage plays: *A Doubtful Paradise* and *The Enemy Within* (Abbey Theatre)	
	1963 With Tyrone Guthrie in Minneapolis; *The Blind Mice* (Olympia Theatre, Dublin)	
	1964 *Philadelphia, Here I Come!* (Gaiety Theatre, Dublin)	**1964** Death of Brendan Behan
		1965 John B. Keane, *The Field*

Events in Ireland	Author's life	Literary events
	1966 *The Gold in the Sea* (short stories); *The Loves of Cass McGuire* (Helen Hayes Theatre NY)	
	1967 *Lovers* (Gate Theatre, Dublin)	
1968 First Civil Rights March	**1968** *Crystal and Fox* (Gaiety)	
1969 Outbreak of sectarian and political conflict, N Ireland	**1969** *The Munday Scheme* (Olympia)	**1969** Howard Brenton, *The Romans in Britain* (play)
	1971 *The Gentle Island* (Olympia)	
1972 'Bloody Sunday' in Derry		**1972** John Montague, *'A Lost Tradition'*
	1973 *The Freedom of the City* (Royal Court)	
	1975 *Volunteers* (Abbey)	**1975** Seamus Heaney, *North*
	1977 *Living Quarters* (Abbey)	
	1979 *Faith Healers* (Longacre Theatre NY); *Aristocrats* (Abbey)	
1980 Ten prisoners starve to death; riots N Ireland	**1980** With Stephen Rea founds Field Day Theatre Co; *Translations* opens in Derry	
	1982 *The Communication Cord* (Guildhall, Derry)	
		1983 Tom Paulin, *The Liberty Tree*
		1985 Frank McGuinness, *Observe the Sons of Ulster Marching Towards the Somme*
	1988 *Making History* (Guildhall, Derry)	
	1990 *Dancing at Lughnasa* (Abbey)	
	1994 *Molly Sweeney* (Gate); Friel resigns from Field Day	
	1997 *Give Me Your Answer, Do!* (Abbey)	

alienation the feeling of being estranged or isolated, or not at home. It is not just the experience of being an outsider, but can also involve feeling estranged from one's own home, friends, or society. In dramatic terms, alienation can be cultivated in the theatre among audiences in order to prevent them from identifying with particular characters or actions so that they can make their interpretations objectively

antiquity the condition of being able to trace ancient forms and objects, and of belonging to age-old patterns of living and thinking. It involves ignoring the latest changes in all or any fields (e.g. science, dress, art, politics) and paying attention only to how the ancient world lived

characterisation the way in which a writer creates characters in a narrative or drama so as to attract or repel our sympathy

Classics from the Latin for 'writing of the highest quality'. Because Western critics have often regarded ancient Greek and Roman literary works as the models for excellence, 'Classics' came to refer to 'ancient Greek and Roman' literature, culture and history in general

colloquialism relaxed, everyday language, rather than formalised or conventional language. Colloquialisms in literature will often be composed of the use of incorrect grammar, such as 'yous' instead of the plural 'you', and the incorporation of localised or regional language, like the words 'jackeen' or 'eejit' in Ireland. Slang is also part of colloquial language

epic specifically, epic refers to a long narrative poem featuring superhuman heroes, but more generally 'epic' can refer to any piece of literature or drama which involves myths and legends about the foundation and transformation of national communities. Friel's *Translations* might be called a national epic according to this loose definition of the term

Hiberno-English varieties of English spoken in Ireland, where standard English has been altered by contact with the grammatical structures, vocabularies, sound systems, pronunciations and patterns of intonation of the Gaelic language

historical drama a type of drama which is set in a particular historical period, and which dramatises events and attitudes of that period. Both real and imaginary persons may appear as characters

imagery (Latin 'copy, representation') a critical word with several different applications. In its narrowest sense an 'image' is a word-picture, a description of some visible scene or object. More commonly, however, 'imagery' refers to the figurative language in a piece of literature (metaphors and similes); or all the words which refer to objects and qualities which appeal to the senses and feelings

irony saying something while deliberately meaning something completely opposite, or implying a different meaning by understatement and allusion. In *Translations*, Hugh speaks in pompous, eloquent statements about the richness of Gaelic language and literature compensating for the poverty of its speakers, but a careful reading of the way in which he makes these statements may reveal that he says them only to make fun of Yolland's naïve romantic attitudes towards Ireland

malapropism the unwitting use of improper or muddled words, deployed by the author for comic effect – from Mrs Malaprop in Sheridan's *The Rivals*

modernity the condition of being in current fashion or being in touch with the most recent developments in all or any fields (e.g. science, dress, art, politics). It may also mean a healthy disrespect for anything antiquated and a keen interest in experimenting with newness

subtext a situation that lies behind the behaviour of characters in a play, but to which no-one refers explicitly and which may never be fully explained

symbolism objects or images which come to stand for something else. A tree, for example, can symbolise strength or tradition, while white lilies conventionally symbolise death or mourning. Symbolist literature tends to emphasise the importance of using private and conventional symbols to create a wider meaning or world-view

tragedy the genre in literature and drama which conventionally involves works in which an individual is seen to have a lamentable downfall, sometimes as a scapegoat or as a sacrifice. In *Translations*, a whole community is the subject of a tragic downfall, as its culture and ways of life are seen to be sacrificed to make way for the desires of its conquerors

AUTHOR OF THIS NOTE

John Brannigan is lecturer in Irish studies and literary studies at the University of Luton, where he teaches courses on Irish drama, postcolonial writing and the relationship between literature and history. He is the author of the York Note on Joyce's *Dubliners*, and is co-editor of *Re: Joyce*, a collection of essays which reflects contemporary responses and approaches to Joyce. He has also published work on contemporary literary theories, the literature of 1950s Britain and a number of Irish writers, including W.B. Yeats and Brendan Behan. He is currently preparing an anthology of colonial and anticolonial writings about Ireland.